The Waterfront Writers

GEORGE BENET

ROBERT CARSON

GENE DENNIS

KEN FOX

JAMES HAMILTON

ASHER HARER

HERB MILLS

J. PRICE

DAVE RAMET

photographs by
LEONARD MALLIETT
BRIAN NELSON
FRANK SILVA
MICHAEL VAWTER

The Waterfront Writers

The Literature of Work

Edited by **Robert Carson**

Published in San Francisco by
Harper & Row, Publishers
New York   Hagerstown   San Francisco   London

FIRST EDITION

Designed by Paul Quin

Library of Congress Cataloging in Publication Data
    Main entry under title:

    The Waterfront Writers.

    1. Stevedores' writings, American. 2. American literature—California—San Francisco. 3. American literature—20th century. 4. Waterfronts—California—San Francisco—Literary collections. I. Carson, Robert, 1945–
        II. Waterfront Writers.
PS508.S83W37   1979   810'.8'0923875   79–1772
ISBN 0–06–250130–5

---

79 80 81 82 83 10 9 8 7 6 5 4 3 2 1

Contents

CONTENTS

The Larger World: Gathering in the Nets · 139

Introduction

This collection presents an art that follows the lines of life: the tumult of images, depressions, explosions, reflections, the tender, the brutal.

> The last heavy-veined leaf
> from all the branches of thought—
> A working partner pummeled to eternity
> head first in a glorious swan dive
> From the bow of the ship.
> Dull thud we all pretended
> Not to hear.

> San Francisco skyline, undisturbed
> contraditions of building, city floating
> in fog at the beltline of TransAmerica.

The experience and images that give force and focus to *The Waterfront Writers* are based on the realities of life. They continue beyond fact to symbol and meaning.

The Waterfront Writers and Artists is a group of worker-artists. They exist in vigorous contradiction to the notion of "artistes" inhabiting an ivory highrise isolated and insulated from any sordid grubbing for a livelihood or the mundane facts of life. They also defy the "hard-hat" image and Archie Bunker lifestyle that the image-mongers decree as role models for the American worker.

We have our own images of ourselves and our fellow workers as diverse as the characters that generate them. I am known as Big Red, and I've worked ships for fifteen years, along with Flugo, the Commander, Strong Arm Louie, the Old Ranger, Crazy Jack, Moanin' Jack, Drugstore Larry, Bicycle Larry, Shovel Mouth, and Hardrock. All of them are good storytellers, and every name has a story. Some are veterans of the Big Strike in 1934 or the sociopolitical causes that are a part of our union history. They all taught me that progress and change are not products, created by wizards with T-squares, but processes.

My work is the movement of cargo, but I function as a person not a piece of machinery. I do not prostrate myself before progress or accept my work style's increasing routinization as an inevitable "good." Sophocles, over two thousand years ago, criticized those concerned only with the machinations of power and the amassing of "goods":

> But rule over men, not over a dead city!
> Ships are only hulls, citadels are nothing,
> When no life moves in the empty passageways.
>
> (*Oedipus Rex,* Prologue)

The technocrat, computer printout in hand, might evaluate the sail as an archaic, outmoded means of propulsion. But the involved vision of the artist portrays it as "Canvas wings beating down the sky."

As workers, we stand at the juncture between a colorful past and a mechanized, routinized future. Old work ways, carriers of personal power and identity, depart like soft footfalls in a cemetery. Is it inevitable that we accept the computer readout of our probable future with total submission to the oracles of technology? The promised utopia of wealth and leisure produced by servant machines without the taint of human hands or error does not attract me as a person.

As workers, the Waterfront Writers and Artists help to produce, maintain, and change the society we inhabit. As writers and artists, we work to create a fuller understanding and insight into that society. We have a special perspective on the American scene as a result of unique historical and artistic conditions. We draw from a union tradition reaching back through a series of sociopolitical stands to the San Francisco General Strike of 1934 (one of only two general strikes in U.S. history). Because of our function in processing world goods, we see global crises heating up by observing the flow of cargo (munitions flowing out to Pacific wars, caskets returning).

The lure and lore of the sea has always been central to the imagery of American art and letters. The Waterfront Writers draw from this rich fund of images and the oral tradition and folklore shared by seamen and longshoremen.

The group's concern with change and the necessity of change in work styles and lifestyles is a national concern. People are realizing the need to control their physical, social, and emotional environments; they are seeking noncompulsive lives. The work in this collection, representing selections from every literary genre, will give the reader some sense of the problem of trying to hold on to human values in a dehumanized and automated environment.

The group was founded on the principle that work need not stifle art. Instead, it can inspire and enrich the artist's vision of the world at large. It forces the artist's participation in life and social processes. Esthetics merge with experience and give validity and value to art and work. This breaks the barrier between life and art. Both are made accessible and relevant. They become a part of our daily experience.

The three major divisions in this collection have arisen naturally, the way a typical public reading held by Waterfront Writers would proceed: first, work and workers; second, family, life, introspection; third, more universal themes and the world we all share.

It is time for workers, artists, intellectuals—for every person—to review the facts of their lives, their stories, histories, and myths. From this material a new literature can evolve, more relevant to the daily lives of people as they are. And from this strong foundation we can move confidently into a future illuminated by a sure sense of our past and potential—directed, but not compelled. Otherwise, we would, like Icarus, find ourselves descending "upon new monstrosities—without wings."

Robert Carson
Pier 80, San Francisco
1979

Work and Workers

A Bill of Sale

Eight or seven years ago,
before my back
began to scream at night,
we worked a rusted freighter
held together by forgotten screws.

The cargo was burlap bags of coffee
and the lingering heat of Latin suns.
Spilled beans became
ball bearings beneath our feet
as we swung the sacks
into bulging stacks on pallet boards.

The talk was of other lives
and private selves
with dreams of suburbs
and hard-fought football games.

An older brother heard something
in my own embroidered tale
and said, What's
a nice, educated boy like you
doing in a job like this?
I said then,
and pray it can be said at the end,
I sold my body
to save my mind.

Footnotes to the Glory Years

No massage
has ever reached
the chronic crick
chiseled in my neck
by forever looking up
from the lower hold
in fear of falling loads
and tumbling booms;
untied the stomach knot
where I carry
the sound Big Sam made
when he got pounded
into a blood-red puddle
falling four decks
from a broken ladder;
erased the sight
of Leroy's face
when he got skewered
by falling steel
at the army base,
and Baby Erik's thumb
tacked forever
to a redwood log
by a careless crowbar.

My soul
has been sucked dry
and suffocated by
the shadow of a
forty-foot container,
Restored by outrage
at the mindless technology
unleashed by cash register computers.

So logical,
so methodical,
casting aside bent bodies

with poisoned lungs
to proceed with greed.
So technologically correct.
A heritage
caved in by the
ponderous pounding
of some psychopathic
robotonic
beast
clothed in the niceties
of contractual compromise.

Friday's paycheck
somehow softens the anger.
The next contract
will put things right.
After all,
it wasn't me that died.
I'm too quick and smart
to go that way.
Besides,
I'm immune to asbestos dust
and monoxide fumes.
Big Sam
was probably drunk.
Erik's an arrogant asshole.
And Leroy—
not watching the game,
as usual.

Me and my partners
are splitting
for a month in Mexico
next January
when work slacks off.

Soreness and sorrow
dissipate in dreams
of an Acapulco sunrise.
It seems that
rage is out
this year.

DAVE RAMET

Coffee Hatch

Back roll the hatch covers,
Down the ladder-tunnels we huddle,
Tear apart the paper over
Coffee sacks' many-ported muddle.

Dig with your hooks and fingers
One hundred and eighty pounds high
On pallet boards and rope slings,
Winch them toward the sky.

Here swings a load of pallets
Penduluming across the square,
To bang your head like a butcher's mallet
If poor foresight hangs you there.

Watch the fat sling brush the coaming
Dodge the bags as they fly
Thirty feet down they shoot homing
At gravity's bid that you die.

Five o'clock—what do you say,
After pumping heavy coffee today—
That because work's slow in the hall
You'll be back tomorrow after all?

Slow Time in the Hiring Hall

Talk—Talk a wide mouth, square-toothed, jut jaw
moves up and around a tight-lipped smirk,
While a slack-jaw smile listens to the jive.

Bare light-bulb thoughts
make the bench even harder to sit on,
and the "Jive" is nothing but "Two Word Down,"
No "Ups" when the work is slow!

Listen to "Fat Lips" con the game
with a slap of the deck and "Who's Dealing?"
The table's quiet, save for the rustling of an old paper
with the ink read off of it. Nobody takes the challenge!

Headline talk is done. Lips turn down, and one by one,
Like a chant, they cry "No Work!"
Twiddled thumbs and tapping fingers mingle
with twitched eyelids,
and the boredom sinks in LIKE THUNDER!

DAVE RAMET

Vans, Rain, and Wind

Used to be we'd unload Spanish cinnamon, Egyptian cotton,
Costa Rican coffee, and Scotch scotch from
Cavernous bellies of rusty ships.

Not now.

Whiz kids with T-squares, slide rules, and
Whips whirl warehouse cargo box and ship
Into new flat square molds.

We stand at night on a man-made spit
In the air in the middle of the bay,

And when the wind slides rain as you
Lash the tops of the cargo box it's all
You can do to stay

Where you are.

ROBERT CARSON

Old Sailor Looking at a Container Ship

At bend of bay
Sail voices in the wind
Fog's slow spiral under the bridge
He sees containers overall.
All the same shape, all the same size.
Loaded from a flat obtrusive yard;
Cut from the city by cyclone fencing.

He remembers sixty years ago,
Time cutting through him
Like a knife.
Silver blade clear as
Light on the open sea;
And against the horizon
Canvas wings
Beating down the sky.

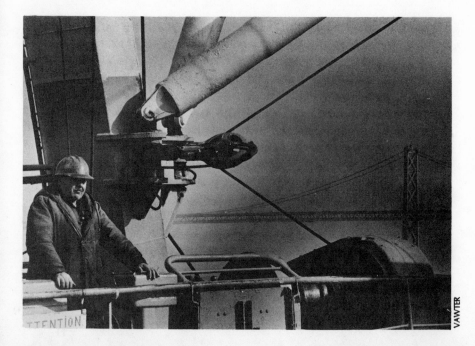

VAWTER

Clerks' Shack (Pier 9)

Sitting in a barren brain box
Built with two-by-fours.
A lighted light bulb
Casts its ugly rays
upon
Eclipsed Eyes
that see
Nothing
to
hear
Nothing
to
say.
Except sit upon a
Pedestal of
Fatty
Flesh
and think
Nothing,
to do.
Nothing,
except,
Sit in a
barren brain box.
Limbo for a
Day's
Wage.

Rain, Cotton, and the Walking Boss

The storm ripped the rain tent
And we all lay back

'Cause you can't load cotton in the rain.

Lener looked around, saw us sitting on a fence
Of bales of cotton, just like his audience
He thought, and began his loud-mouthed yell:

"Those students at Berkeley, what the hell
Are we doing supporting the bums,
Unpatriotic, demonstrating, intellectual crums?"

As I had attended a class or two,
To put a little light in dock's dark day,
I spoke in defense of study and truth,
And of workers' right to learn and to pay
For the rich man's educational fruit.

Lener with his almanac, I with my memory,
Clashed like cargo hooks, rasped like emory,
Filled the cotton-muted dock with ninety decibels,
Or at least he did; I calmly countered with Nietzsche's free will
And Freud's expression of the id.

Six months later a brother shook my hand,
Told me how he'd told his wife.
How on that stormed and cottoned night
He'd had the time of his life
Watching Lener and me fight,

And seeing education win it in the end.

DAVE RAMET

Steel Job

Black ship, men and night,
Molten orbs center light,
Shack shadows old man's fright,
Holding young jumping might,
Beams scream and swing at height,
Placed! All back to moth-sight.

VAWTER

Loading Rice at 14th Street

My eyes focused
(confused)
registering the ship,
the hatch,
the tons of rice
bound blindingly
belly up
in white one hundred
pound sacks.

Wild Bill's watch
pointed to eleven o'clock.

An hour had slipped by
with the silence
of a daydream.

Stirred by the whirring winches,
nurtured by a
rare working rhythm,
a muscled mantra had
released my mind
in meditative elegance,
leaving behind the day,
the sun, the sacks,
my hands, the pallet
boards, my back.

For this hour
there were no wages,
no boss, no bills,
no carburetor trouble,
or contract violations.

No need to think,
just to move by instinct
as heart and head
fused and flew
star grazing
in galactic pastures,
then returned
to make this a day
I'd have paid to work.

Pier 26—Longshore Lunch Room

It's a dark Dank Day
For sitting in a Five-Table Room
With Ten Long Benches
That no one else is sitting on.

It's Abysmally Dysmal,
Graffittied walls
Speckled with Crushed Bugs,
Spittle and Beer.
Table Tops covered with
Thick layers of
Decayed Lunch.

One light,
too bright to look at,
too Dark to read by.
No windows!
No Nothing!
The Lone Radiator
Heats itself and
Nothing else.
Darkened corners of uncollected
Garbage give off
Foul Odors of Past
Activity.

I sit waiting for the
Next job and try—
Desperately—to Daydream
Myself out of existence.

Monopoly Capital and the Interpenetration of Imperial Markets at Pier 27

Eight o'clock.
Walking along the pier:
Bargain tiers of
banded bales of
shredded American rags
en route to India.
Yesterday's Levi's
and Percale prints,
soon to return
rewoven
as Madras shirts
and bedspreads in
a Macy's catalogue.

The gangway rattles
ahead
behind
beneath
me.
A depression-gray day.
Cold.
A hell of a day
for a freezer job.

Nothing special
about Number Three Hatch.
Smells and feels
the same it did
last voyage.
The lower 'tween deck
cluttered with bits
of broken pallet board,
a bent shackle,
curlicues
of banding wire
askew;

cast aside in the frenzy
to discharge African cargo
at a southern port.

The ship's mate
creaks down the ladder
to unlock the freezer
and scatters frozen air.
Pacific Rim Cargo is
hoisted aboard erratically
(This is the final shift:
Supervisors scrounge
dock and warehouse
for an extra pound
of freight, another penny).

Time for a smoke,
the locker nearly full:
Fourteen tons of
Swanson Chicken Dinners
for the American
officers' club in Taiwan
(breasts, thighs, drumsticks);
Six tons of wings, necks, and backs
bulk packed
bound for Sonny's Supermarket
on Pago Pago;
three tons of chicken stomachs,
a gift from the White House
to the poor of Bangkok.

Where
I wonder,
did they put
the feet and heads?

COME ON UP TO THE
NEXT DECK, shouts
the gang boss down
the hatch, WE GOT SOME
UNIT LOADS OF PET FOOD
FOR SINGAPORE.

Ambience

Kicked artists off the Northern Waterfront.
   Want to maintain the view.
No ship ever stood over us like
   the buildings they've planned.
Moved the Eagle Cafe to a second level
   of a complex built by a taco king.
Pushed longshoremen to the thirteenth floor
   of a twelve-story building.
Brought consultants from LA to tell us
   the social esthetics of our own territory.
Sure, they're going to serve up a
   Longshoreman's Brunch.
   View the Bay.
   Unmolested.
   No workers.
Champagne cocktails, clean fingernails,
Croissants, and—imagine Clipper Ships.

I know they want our sweat trapped
Under the plastic tops
Of their hatchcover tables.

KEN FOX

Three PM (On the Docks)

The Afternoon is here
and halfway through—
Three PM and Coffee Time

No Motors Running
No Sounds of Work
My head is full of
Counting Boxes.
I'm tired the rest
of the Day
Creeps till
Five.

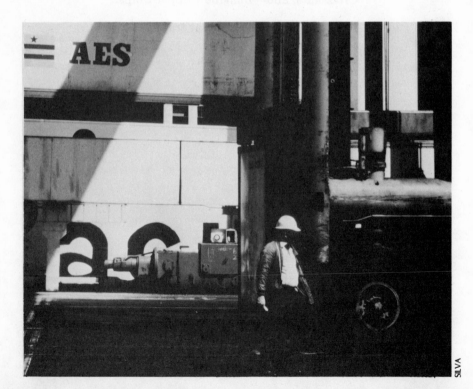

SILVA

I Guess we are
Not so different
after all—
For those
Around me feel
just the
Same

I wondered once
How many hours
Should be needed
for a
Day's Pay.
I've come to the
conclusion
that if they were
all worked when one
felt good—
We'd work until we
Died

I'm sort of glad
That there are those
that are
Bad
Then I know each day will
end and
some Part of It
will be
For Me

Exiles of the City

When I was born in San Francisco, there were
long shadows cast still from a General Strike, a World War.
Memories flared on the lit end of cigars.
Always the puff and swollen fires, men's breath,
the city would breathe and choke and hustle
to the rhythms—newspaper hawkers,
the whiz-spin of rollers sending endless
boxes into dark holes in trucks and ships.

Women fresh from the war plants, assembly-line slavery,
cranked out the children—buggys and strollers
left alone in the sun on the pavement,
as if to exile us and teach us early about
the wind and fog and salt, the cool hands of the street.
Soon we fingered, with false bravado,
the handles of knives, roamed in packs,
danced to the tune of mass production:
the factories and ours.

Each birthday party a Nationalist feast:
Italian, French, Irish, Philippino, Indian.
Somehow it all drew together, breathing in all
something of the gypsy, something of the Arts.
All had their hands on the rollers, gears, switches,
winches of the city.

There were the constant sailings and homecomings.
Maybe, we thought, beyond the ice-man (black-slick apron)
beyond the butcher (blood-stained apron), even beyond the
rollers, warehouses, docks, and the space between
the bridges we could find the world growing out,
opened naturally like spring and flowers and trees.
Sailors brought the tales, and we hornpiped them
through the streets. Snaking through the sunlight,
tasting smells, the salt and bread, excited our blood,
soon we made connections with the bay, black connections,
down so far we compressed, squeezed in a mass,

learned of people who slept under foundations deep in the city,
fish with bigger gills, fire-bomb at the end of the
tokay rainbow, eyes exploded, puffed and bloated,
belly up on the beaches.

Nothing remains the same—coming home from work and war
and the sea—knowing the lines of ocean's poem,
or breath in the sail. Distant and longer shadows.
The fog that laces in and out: Coast's continual breathing
ritual with interior valleys.
Some return in airless plastic bags
With name tags to match the death letters
And the neatness of automation processing
Bodies wrapped in vinyl
We raised cargo nets, nets around the city,
teaming with goods and fish and life.
Knife slashing edges, the sting of salt and blood.

Suddenly a loosening, the faintest falling,
Simple remembrances: sun and ice, cement and salt
The last heavy-veined leaf from all the branches of thought.
Tremulous journey to earth.
Blowing down past the office buildings,
black-glass-garbled reflections of ships and bay and fog,
life we never knew.

We return to the tolling of bells,
buoyed in every night,
church bells, buoy bells, ships' bells.
Narrowing lanes from sea to the city.
Sliding between missing sounds of dreams we never built.
The leaf scratching down the streets,
Whirling the tones of our own exile.

Excerpts from A Rat's-Eye View of History

Storytelling on the San Francisco Waterfront

Every longshoreman has been involved in a host of on-the-job encounters that for one reason or another he has subsequently related to others. Such events are simply a part of the job. As a result, each of us has been provided the raw materials from which we have fashioned a number of stories about life on the San Francisco docks. By the same token, every man who has gone longshoring has become something of a storyteller.

Some of the stories recount an event that the storyteller feels should be known and remembered by his fellow longshoremen, if not, indeed, by others. Such stories are essentially intended to convey a lesson or at least an observation about our working and union life. They are consciously didactic, if usually very modestly so. However, stories of this sort also routinely undergo an evolution and elaboration with each retelling, because the men who hear them typically subject the storyteller's understanding to some refinement. For this reason, such stories are really a collective product of the waterfront.

As might be supposed, we also tell these stories to the woman or women in our lives, to our children, and to other friends. We do this, once again, because we imagine them to be instructive. On the other hand, it is never very easy to explain why a story has been changed since last told. Upon inquiry, we may simply mask our own confusion and embarrassment by saying, "Well, it's still true. Fact is, it's even truer this way. Actually, it's getting truer all the time. And besides, it's a better story now."

When a story deals with something the storyteller has come to especially value, it often happens that the man who emerges as its central figure has died since the time of the event. Indeed, the first full telling of such a story is not infrequently occasioned by the death of that figure. In this circumstance, the story is, of course, a memorial and eulogy. It is the way the storyteller and his listeners both remember and bury their dead. And in this modest and unhurried ceremony, they look again—however briefly—at their own existence.

These stories may be viewed as genuine folk stories, partly by reason of the common, everyday events they recount. They may also be viewed in this way because of the audiences to which they are essentially addressed, their occasion and intent, the manner of their evolution, and, of course, their source of validation. Like any story, they vary in their generality. They also vary in the significance that is collectively assigned to them by the storyteller and those who listen. However, they may finally be viewed as folk stories because they invariably give witness to something those persons have come to value in themselves and others. By the same token, they intrinsically deal with things that are in some measure to be opposed. For these reasons, they are at once both autobiographical and social, personal and political, enigmatic and simple. They may again be brutal and reflective, cynical and hopeful, saddening and heartening. In a word, these stories are a collective expression of the consciousness which Bertolt Brecht once called for: "a rat's-eye view of history."

The life we have known as longshoremen and the history of which we have fashioned stories has, of course, been complex and contradictory. However, something of that life and history—and therefore something of the existence we have known by reason of our work and our union with one another—may at least be suggested by the on-the-job encounters that will now be depicted.

Encounter 1

Setting

On the offshore, weather deck rail of a vessel.

Cast

A walking boss who had grown up in a small lumber port on the Oregon coast. Prior to his landing on the San Francisco waterfront in the mid-1920s, he had sailed aboard the steam lumber schooners that plied the West Coast. This Finn had a favorite observation: "You know, we use more dunnage on a job like this than we loaded aboard them schooners." This man liked people, and people liked him. They liked to kid him, too, because it always seemed that he had "been around for years and years." People would ask him to tell about discharging the Mayflower and loading the Golden Hinde.

Four holdmen, all of whom had been in the industry about six months. They were on the rail waiting for the hoist of a heavy piece of machinery from a barge which was moored alongside the vessel. They had been talking about the civil rights demonstrations that were then being conducted at various places of business in downtown San Francisco.

Event

The walking boss went to the rail to see what was happening aboard the barge. He overheard the discussion.

The walking boss (having leaned against the rail and having been implicitly invited into the discussion): "You know, it's no different than what's happening down here. People aren't going to be denied their places any more and especially since the government and all the politicians are always talking about how free and democratic we are. And it's happening on a lot of things. Three days ago I had a fellow on the job that had hair to his shoulders. So, 'long about coffee time the superintendent says to me, "How's Goldie Locks doing?" "Well," I says to him, "He's doing God-damned well, that's how he's doing. He's doing the work, and he wants to learn, so I don't give a damn how he does his hair. Fact is, he's doing a whole lot better than some people that don't have any hair." So, we all got to loosen up and that's what I told him and that's what I tell myself, too. There's a whole lot happening in this world, now."

One of the men, with the glint that comes from poking fun at somebody who is very much liked and respected: Well, you sure done your union duty, Bro._____. There you were, tellin' some company guy that things are changing and that it ain't like when the *Mayflower* was coming into port.

Walking boss: Well, that's right. That's exactly what I told him, but now I'm telling you that some things stay the same.

Longshoreman: What do you mean by that?

Walking boss: It's simple. Der boss and der header-upper has still got a job of keeping his eye on things and turning people to. So, let's look alive, 'cause that hoist is ready.

Encounter 2

Setting
The lower hold of a conventional, break-bulk vessel.

Cast
Three men who had gone to work on the waterfront in 1959.

Event
Having stowed some cargo, the eight holdmen who were working the job had proceeded to lay lengths of 1″ x 12′ lumber atop that cargo. Such lumber is called *dunnage*. It helps prevent the shifting of cargoes stowed beneath it and on top of it. It is provided the ship by the contracting stevedore company and hoisted aboard as needed. Having completed this work, the men retired to the offshore wing to await additional cargoes. As always, they began to converse as they sat and waited.

First man: You know, they just don't use dunnage the way they used to. Fact is, nobody gives a damn about a lot of things anymore. Christ, I was on a ship a couple of weeks ago that had some shifted cargo in the upper 'tween deck of number two and it never was re-stowed. That ship went back out the Gate just like she'd come in. Now, that's a fucking disgrace. I guess it all comes down to competing against the container, but one thing's for sure. Nobody gives a damn.

Second man: You've got a point there, partner, but there's no sense bullshitting about it, either. A lot of us so-called longshoremen never did like laying dunnage. We were too busy bullshitting each other about laying pipe and things like that. You know yourself, laying dunnage can mean a whole lot of work. And that means for everybody. There's no four men working and four men off when it comes to dunnage.

Third man: Actually, you've both got a point, but this puts me in mind of a job I ought to tell you about 'cause everybody got real involved with dunnage. I was in gang twenty-eight. Christ, it must have been ten years ago. Well, anyway, we caught a job at Pier 23. It was a Jap ship with plenty of general cargo and there was this mate that kept hanging over the coaming calling for dunnage. "More dunnage. More dunnage." All morning long, there he was on the coaming with "More dunnage, more dunnage." So, more dunnage it was and then some cargo and there he was, back again, with

"More dunnage, more dunnage." Jesus, he was really gettin' everybody pissed off. I remember old John Carter. He was the walking
boss. I remember now, John died about four months later, but he
sure got agitated that day. He got on the coaming with that mate
and started stomping around and waving his arms and hollering
the way he always loved to do. "What do you mean, 'More dunnage, more dunnage?'" But that mate, you know, he just smiled
and came right back with "More dunnage, please. More dunnage,
Mr. Boss." So, naturally, us hold men are watching all of this and
finally one of the guys yells up to him, "Say, Comrade Mate, what
the hell are you doing back home, building a house?" Well, that
fucking mate, Christ, I'll never forget, he gets this great big grin on
his face and comes right back with "No. Need barn!" Well, naturally, we got a helluva kick out of that, so, more dunnage it was.
Christ, by the time we closed that hatch it was half full of dunnage.

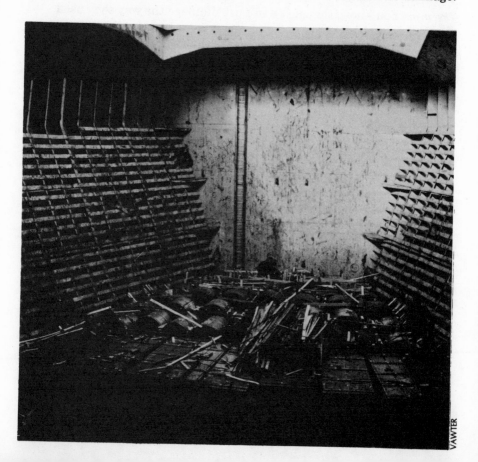

VAWTER

And it was the best, too, 'cause when we found out what he had in mind, we got word to the dock men and naturally they didn't send us nothing but the best.

First man: Now, that's a good story, fellow worker, and a whole lot better than some you tell. But the thing is, it don't relate to what I'm talking about. Hell, we don't even have good dunnage anymore.

Second man: So, what else is new? What the hell *does* "relate" anymore? It's like a lot of things. We're just gonna have to settle for a good story, but I guess that's better than nothing.

Encounter 3

Setting

A clerk's shack on the dock.

Cast

A walking boss, a super-cargo, and *two longshoremen,* all of whom had known one another for years and all of whom were union veterans from the early 1930s.

Event

A way of passing the time during a standby wait for a truckload of frozen meat scheduled for palletizing.

Supercargo: I think these young people that are coming in are doing real good. I don't see it all, but the work gets done and everybody is pretty friendly. Maybe a little weird, sometimes, but friendly.

Walking boss: I guess so, but there's lots of differences. I don't know what will happen to the union. We packed union stuff and political stuff to read in the hold. Now they got them underground newspapers with them. Christ, them papers are really something.

First longshoreman: What do you care? I see you reading 'em. But, maybe you're just checking them out to make sure they printed your ad. "Very old and grouchy waterfront character desires young, sympathetic, and easily satisfied female companion. Must have big tits."

Second longshoreman: Now, you see. Both of you comrades are still wallowing in sexism and chauvinism. Now, me, I just read them papers to stay informed, see. That's why I'm healthy and you guys are sick. Now, what's really bothering you two is these young people are having more fun than we did. Actually that's what annoys the piss out of a lot of old people. But see, what you guys don't realize is that those young people over in Berkeley and up in Haight-Ashbury are really on your side. Why, there's a group that's working right now for sex in the geriatrics ward and for broke-down stevedores. Shit. That's all part of the revolution and it's part we didn't see, see?

Walking boss: Can't we please get this back on a serious level?

Second longshoreman: What do you mean, "serious"? What I'm saying is serious. I'm always serious. That's a cross I've borne for years. Serious and concerned.

Walking boss: My ass. But listen, 'cause I want you to tell me what you think about something. OK?

Second man: OK.

Walking boss: OK. So, here's what happened. I had this man on a coffee job at Pier 32 last week and he's sporting that Lenin button. You know, that cameo-type button that's red and gold. OK?

Second man: OK.

Walking boss: So, the men are on deck, re-rigging the gear sometime in the afternoon and I get the chance to ask this fellow, "Say, I was wondering about that button. What is it?" And you know what he said?

Supercargo: He told you to go fuck yourself.

Walking boss: No, he didn't.

First man: Well, he should have.

Walking boss: Maybe so, but he didn't.

Second man: Well, God damn it, man what the hell did he say?

Walking Boss: He told me it was a Mitch Miller Fan Club button. He looked me right in the eye and said, "That's a profile of Mitch Miller." Then he says, "He's a musician, but maybe you know that. Anyway, you join the club, you get a button."

First man: So what did you say?

Walking boss: What the fuck could I say? I said "Oh." So, how about it, Mr. Wisenheimer, what do you say?

Second man: How the hell do I know? Maybe he's crazy. Maybe that's what somebody told him. Good Christ, maybe he was being straight! Maybe that's how people are organizing these days! But, see, the real problem is that you don't know how to approach people.

Walking boss: Oh, is that so?

Second man: Yes, I'm afraid it is. You've got to learn how to approach things and how to handle things.

Walking boss: Oh, Jesus. You know, I sure am glad I had a chance to talk to you about all this, but I'll tell you what.

Second man: What's that?

Walking boss: How about you showing me how to approach that reefer truck that's just now rolling in? And when you get done doing that, why then you can show me how to handle frozen meat. How does that sound?

Second man: Why, that sounds real good. See, I knew you'd have the proper attitude. I just knew it. And that's why I've been spending all this time with you. Now, if you'll just stay out of the way and keep your God-damned eyes open, why then maybe you will learn something. Then, too, see, there's this to consider. Me and John, here, now we're the best in the business. So, naturally, if you can't learn from us, why then you're not going to learn from anybody.

Walking boss: I think that maybe you're the best bull-shitter in the business. I think that maybe that's what we're talking about. But, I do know one thing.

Second man: What's that?

Walking boss: I know I want to learn more over there against that truck than I did here.

Second man: Well, c'mon, then, and let's find out. But remember, stand clear and keep your eyes open, because otherwise we can't do a thing for you.

Encounter 4

Setting

On the weather deck of a "freezer ship," i.e., a ship distinguished by hatches that are completely refrigerated. The vessel was being discharged of frozen meat from Australia and New Zealand.

Cast

A winch driver who went to work on the San Francisco waterfront shortly after his emigration from England in early 1946. A fairly short, stocky, thick-armed, and very outgoing man. A knot of tightly curled red hair and fading freckles. He was wearing shorts, something he frequently did on warm days. As might be supposed, such attire was highly unusual on the San Francisco waterfront, but he was only very occasionally asked about it. That may perhaps be explained by his accent or perhaps his stature and the size of his arms. In any event, his friends and acquaintances got a big kick out of his practice: "He says it's part of his culture. And it's about the only sensible part, too. So, on a hot and sunny day, here he'll come, shorts and all, and sometimes with one of those hats that 'the great white hunters' always wear."

Two holdmen who had been friends since their San Francisco high school days and who had worked as partners during their eight months on the waterfront. Both are in their mid-twenties and both are sporting big, drooping mustaches.

Event

The winch driver had just got off the winches to begin his afternoon relief period. The holdmen had just climbed out of their hatch so as to "thaw out." The three of them meet on the offshore rail opposite the hatch they were working so as to take the sun and watch the bay.

The winch driver (with a big, ready smile): Well, now, must strike you lads as a very relative world. Here I am, all decked out in shorts and fit for the beach and there you are freezin' your bloody arses off.

One of the holdmen, as he sheds a heavy, fur-lined foul-weather coat: You can say that again. It's cold as hell down there. Christ, I was gonna run after work, but I think my feet are about to fall off.

Winch driver: Oh, so you're a runner. Ever make that run from the Ferry Building out to the ocean?

Holdman: You mean the bay-to-breakers race? Yeah. I ran it just last month.

Winch driver: Well, I'll be damned, so did I. Christ, it damn near killed me. How'd you do?

Holdman: I finished. That's about all. You been runnin' long?

Winch driver: I used to run when I was a kid, but I hadn't run for years. It was a damn big mistake, too, but, truth to tell, a God-damned woman goaded me into it.

Holdman (who had broken into a smile): What do you mean?

Winch driver: Well, it was this way. I'd been sleeping with this woman up on Taylor Street every now and then and I was up to her place on the Friday night before the race. And naturally, come Saturday morning, I'm in the sack readin' the green sheet. I always read the sports page. Been doing that for years. And then I spots this article on the race, and when I'm done with it I starts tellin' her about it and how I used to run when I was a kid in England. In some of the schools for blokes who'd had a brush or two with the law they used to make a big thing of runnin.' I guess it was to get you all tired out, but I liked it. It kinda grows on you. It's like that picture, "The Loneliness of the Long Distance Runner." Ever see that picture?"

Holdman: No, I never saw it.

Winch driver: Well, it's a good picture, and, if you like runnin', you ought to see it, if you get a chance. But, anyway, runnin' for me was kind of like that, 'cept the guy in the picture thought a lot more about it than I ever did. I guess the people that ran those schools were right. They always said I did things without thinking. But to get back to what I was saying, I starts tellin' this woman about all that runnin' and straight away she comes back with, "Well, you couldn't manage a run like that now, could you?" Jesus, some women sure got a way of missing what you're trying to say and ways of getting at you, too. So, I jumps up and says, "Just you drive me down to the startin' line and then you can damn well meet me at the ocean." Now, naturally, she thought I was crazy and she said so, too, but, to make a long story short, that's what she did and I made the race. Christ, do you know I ran in my swim trunks and, would you believe, a pair of Italian shoes? I could barely walk for nearly a week, but that bitch just goaded me into it.

Holdman (still grinning): I guess you haven't run since.

Winch driver: You're sure right about that. And, what's more, I don't intend to. The most I'll do is maybe a little jogging. I'll jog to the ice box during commercials, that's what I'll do. But, it's funny about runnin', at least for me. I got to runnin' and all that time back home got back in my head. Christ, I'm glad I'm here, but I'd best leave the runnin' to somebody else and I'm sure gonna leave that woman to somebody else.

Second holdman: You weren't too crazy about England?

Winch driver: Well, let's just say the feelin' was mutual. I spent a lot of time bein' in trouble. Nothing really serious, you know, but I mostly had to keep my eye peeled for the constable. That was before the war, actually. I spent a fair amount of time in what they call "borstal." That's where I was doin' all that runnin'. Just like that movie I asked you about. It's like what you call reform school or may be a step or two above that, but then the war came along and they took me into the army. Good Lord, that was somethin', too. I got put into something called the Royal Fusilliers. The 451st Royal Fusilliers, if you please. Now, as far as I'm concerned, regular soldierin' is no picnic, but a sergeant major we had made a practice of sending me over to a disciplinary battalion. Jesus, mate, you've just got no idea what life is like in a disciplinary battalion of the British Army. Or, I should say, maybe you do, but I hope you don't. But, anyway, after the war they let me go to Canada, but that was too damn English for me and they let me come here. My thinkin' was that San Francisco was about as far from merry old England as I could get.

Second holdman: So when did you start longshoring?

Winch driver: That was in the middle of '46. They took me into the union in '48, after the strike. Jesus, that was sure the best thing that ever happened to me, I can tell you. But listen fellows, I've got the break this up and get back on those winches. Break time for me has come and gone.

First holdman: OK, but listen. Your name is Harry, right?

Winch driver: Yes.

First holdman: OK, so Harry, clear somethin' up for me. What the hell is a fusillier, anyway?

Winch driver: I'll be God-damned if I know, mate. I was in that outfit for almost four years and I never did find out. Jesus, it was somethin'. Do you realize I invaded Normandy in chains? It took me three hours of stumblin' around to find the fuckin' corporal that had the keys. But that's another story, so I'll see you guys later.

Encounter 5

Setting
On the weather dock of a vessel, near a hatch coaming.

Cast
A *walking boss* who had long been known for fairly conservative political views, but who had also been very active within the union and on trade union issues for many years.

A recently employed and bearded *longshoreman*.

Event
The longshoreman had come up the hatch ladder to go ashore for a cup of coffee and to make a phone call. The walking boss was on the coaming watching the hold operation. He had watched the man ascend the ladder. As the man walked down the deck toward the gangway, the walker turned to him.

Walking boss: Say, how's it going with that support group for Chavez and the farm workers?

Longshoreman: Pretty good. We make a trip every month to Delano with some dough.

Boss: So, who keeps the books?

Man: Books? There aren't any books to keep.

Boss: Well, who's payrolling the operation?

Man: C'mon. Are you kidding? There's a ledger. One of the guys keeps track that way, and he takes the dough to the bank. There's no payroll to worry about.

Boss: I hear there's going to be more boycotts and demonstrations. What do you hear?

Man: Me? I don't hear shit, but who's payrolling questions like this, the FBI or somebody?

Boss: Hey, wait a minute. Hold on, now. I'm only kidding. Hell, I support them boycotts.

Man: Well, maybe so, but you sure got a piss-poor way of kidding people. I'll see you later. I got to go phone Moscow.

Encounter 6

Setting

On the center aisle of a cargo shed against which a coffee ship is being discharged.

Cast

A walking boss who had been on the front since the mid-1920s, who had been deeply involved in the union struggles of the 30s and 40s, and early 50s, and who was widely and affectionately viewed as "really quite a character."

Two young men, both with longish hair. They are wearing "Get Out of Viet Nam" buttons.

Event

The walking boss is sauntering down the aisle. He pauses to speak to the two men who are dock-piling the sling-loaded coffee.

Walking boss (first with mock seriousness and then with a smile): Listen, fellow workers. We're going to finish a little bit early, so, I've been thinking. Why don't you guys get the girls, I'll get the grass, and let's go to Berkeley and lay down in front of a troop train?

One of the men (with a big grin, a glance at his partner, and a shake of his head): Take a fuckin' hike, you old goat.

A Home for Herman

Herman retires
first of next month.
Worked the waterfront
as best he could
with cataracts
creaking lungs
and arthritic crystals
in his knees.

Herman was my
gang boss (a
longshoreman's foreman)
for over a year.
We got along good;
had some gentle conversations
about his fresh dead son
and catfish catching
in the Delta slough.

He'd squint through
the sun, grin around
godawful gapacious teeth,
and get gleefully tongue-tied
telling breaktime stories.

Herman liked to be liked
and did his fair share
of liking right back,
but got nervous and loud
when supervision came by.
His good eye would blink,
the dead one would wander;
he'd wheeze on his words
and wiggle his head
sweet-talking the big boss
at the expense of the men,
Bending in breezes of fear
born out of ignorance of
the right thing to do.

When the heat died down
he'd stand there alone,
put a shine on his hard hat
straighten his buttons,
reach out with a joke
to cover his fumbling
betrayal of the men,
tell detailed tales
of improvements on his
mobile home
(rolled years ago
onto a suburban parking lot
with two shade trees
and a cinder-block clubhouse
for the permanent tenants).

Herman was proud of his past,
working warehouses
and grain terminals
or interminable stretches
at sea.
But most of all
he took to the waterfront
and looked to our gang
as part of his family;
puff up paternal
when we'd get praise
from on top; turn to
in the morning pressed
in tan khakis (except
the days he smoked menthol,
when he'd dress all in green).
Chain smokes he does—
you can see his pale arteries
constrict on the inhale,
hear them expand when he'd
walk on the ship.

Herman retires
first of next month
if
he doesn't die first
from arterial confusion.

Albino Charlie's Widow

Anyone could bring
the beer and beans,
but only Charlie
could bring the dreams.

His nonsense
made sense to none
but one
and she survived.

All she had
were his sketches
on a pad
and the bed
where he lay dead.

Lew Welch

Ran into Lew Welch
old beat poet friend of mine
laid my sad story on him
how my mother had died
and my wife and I divorced
and my daughter had married
and how I was at my lowest
psychological ebb
how I started drinking again
as I was lonely.
I told him I met a woman
who interested me
but dealing with her was like
playing handball without walls
our lifestyles differed
our temperaments clashed.
Besides, she dated other men.
Lew said he knew a witch in Bolinas
who could exorcize all my bad luck.
I thought dealing with a witch
would be
the coldest snake I ever touched.

He said
your trouble is
you are a short fat alcoholic longshoreman
from the Mission district
a cigarsmoking horseplaying sonofabitch
and worst of all
an incurable romantic.
Besides . . . I didn't have
any frame of reference
didn't belong to any generation
lost, beat, hip.

I told him he was
a part-time junkie
a part-time waterfront clerk
a part-time alcoholic
a part-time cynic
a part-time poet
and worst of all
a suburbanite
'cause he lived in Marin City.

Why, he asked
if a carpenter does carpentry
and a bridge builder builds bridges
and a banker makes money
well why
does a poet
have to immerse himself in a world of commerce
and shipping?
I said, I love that phrasing—
immerse oneself in a world of commerce and shipping.

Lew said, let's have another gin and tonic
then I gotta go on a long walk.
We had four more gin and tonics
and he walked from the Eagle Cafe
and I never saw him again
no, not on this planet
no, never again.

Lew Welch

Turkey gullet. Gaunt esthetic face.
Stubble and shadow offset his eyes.
Gael waiting for the gale
to ride him out.
Brazen Wings.

I remember him.
Hickory shirt, hair turning gray.
Passing time in our casket-cold workplace.

Warm, wine-flushed, he gave me a copy
of his poems titled "Courses."
Stopping me on the Embarcadero
he made a masterful production out of
the giving and choosing of gift.
He'd been making many such donations
for no declared reason.
I didn't know it was our last exchange.

His words winding endless spaghetti-strand thoughts,
he'd look toward North Beach, leaving our work
at his back. Thoughts in flights of poetry there.
His Adam's apple punched out as he swallowed
remembrances whole.

We went to a bar. Discussed new dimensions
for the writing of words and making of books.
Shuffled thoughts like cards, and suddenly
he threw the deck out.
"We're still building pyramids for the Pharoahs."
He was getting weepy. I looked where he looked.
New buildings going up, old crumbling piers.
Men hauling lines and rigging gear on ships.
A huge crate was landed on deck.

"Still building pyramids," he flew on.
He downed another drink, popped a pill for
his stomach, and joked from the tension and
incongruities of working for a wage, working as a poet.

Sky falling into the bay.
Buildings contradicting the heavens.
He took another pill.
"Man," he said, rolling his eyes, swilling a drink,
"I must be the only hippie in the world
who has to take anti-acid pills."

VAWTER

Sailing Date: *(Revised Version)*

The front room of the flat was silent and dark with the shades drawn. He entered with an oil lamp that flickered, wavered in the stale air. His eyes drew close to the flame for a moment, and he looked almost cross-eyed at the weave of the thick wick. In the weave was something that took his memory back with swelling round feelings in his brain. The *Canberra*, the *Canberra* leaves today, he thought.

He put the lamp on the coffee table in front of him. Its light revealed a living room of almost frightening colors, as if it was planned that way by some odd, brooding intellect. Dark colors in paisley curls on the couch seemed almost alive in their spermatozoic design. The whole room floated on waves of light. He felt it almost impossible to sit down without feeling as though he was sinking in, sinking into something he did not know but could only feel and roll with, sometimes letting it overwhelm him.

Beside the lamp on the coffee table, there was a manuscript he had written called *Sailing Date*. Its contents did not say what he intended it to say, and, he thought, it was a rotten story, an unnervingly rotten, cruddy story. He had tried for weeks to write it, and it grew and grew like a hot air balloon until it finally exploded, leaving the fragments that now lay before him. It was supposed to be great, like the experience it was built around. But he felt that, at least, it was only a rough translation of what happened.

He opened his mouth, stretching the skin tight around his jaw bone, as if to shout something. But what came out came in slow, deliberate, whispering tones. "I cannot capture what happened to me and the old man," he said. "We were so beautiful together, and then it all ended. The old man had tears in his eyes, and he was telling me to go my own way. He was sorry for his generation, but he kept insisting that they had tried. The *Canberra* was leaving in an unexplainable silence like a coffin that was being floated out to sea while watchers tightened their lips, trying to hold the tears back. We heard nothing but the intermittent lapping of waves on the pier pilings. As we stood on a bulkhead between Pier 35 and Pier 37, the ship's long, full body momentarily filled the gap between the two docks, and the old man left, telling me he wanted to remember the ship in that position, so he could have a full picture of it as its shadow almost touched us. I stayed and watched, hearing a faint and hypnotic hum from the *Canberra's* engine room, and I knew what he meant. I just knew it in a solid, whole feeling as the ship made its way past Pier 37, letting me see only the aft end and a flag, and under the flag on the hull the words '*Canberra*' and '*London*.' Then it was gone."

He extinguished the flame from the oil lamp and raised the shades to the early rays of the sun. From the windows of the flat, he could see two rectangles-on-end on Russian Hill with a clump of trees that was a small park stuck between them. He wondered if someone was watching him from one of those buildings. To his left was a church with its gold-painted spires showing themselves absurdly as the sunlight reached only them and not the shadowy, concrete structure below. To his right he could make out the piers on the northern end of the waterfront. They angled out from the city as perfectly as a map might show them. The ships were moored, with night lights and rain tents still rigged.

His mind started flashing myriad diffuse thoughts and pictures, and he moved his head around so fast, back and forth, up and down, that all the buildings started to roll and topple. "You have this disease, see," the doctors had told him, "these flashing things will occur, but if you take care of yourself, get proper rest and all that, you could live to be forty or maybe even fifty." Everytime he flashed, he remembered that. "No strenuous work, no excitement," they said. A life too costly to live, he thought.

The sun was now high enough to flood through the city, stabilizing the buildings, washing down the side streets, lighting the way for the old women slowly walking to church. Black dresses, black coats and scarves. "Say your prayers, and loudly," he called out, "and when the priest says 'I come to the altar of God,' give him the old response and say it loudly, 'To the God who is the joy of my YOUTH.' "

He sat down on the couch, trying to stifle the torrent of emotions that was pushing out of him. He opened a small gold box and withdrew a cigarette. Another coffin nail, so what the hell, he thought. Lighting it, he watched the smoke try to fill the room, but it spread itself too thin and quickly disappeared, leaving only a smell. He glanced at the manuscript again. Something can be done, he thought. Perhaps I need to just get out and watch the *Canberra* leave again.

"Be sure to watch the time," he heard the mate tell a crowd of people, "We sail at eleven AM." His mind flashed a little, and he felt desperate. He wished the coldness of the piers would come inside his body and pacify him.

Porters were scurrying around trying to look concerned as the passengers asked them questions.

"Hey, Doug!" someone called to him. "Hey, Doug, what's doin', man?"

"Nothing. Just watching," he answered.

"Just watching? You're not working here today?"

"No. I've been sick for the last few weeks. I have to wait and see what happens."

"Sick, hmmm. Too bad. Nice-looking girls walking around here. Blonde, blue-eyed. Looks like the school for UCLA cheerleaders. They're all going back to Australia and New Zealand. I bet you came to see all the nice ass, huh?"

"No, nothing like that."

"Man, you're sick, all right."

"Don't sweat about me, Mike. Just play your own game."

"C'mon, Doug. Look—I'm on my break. I'll buy ya a cup of coffee, and we can talk then."

"Next door?"

"Next door."

The restaurant was crowded with a crazy mixture of longshoremen in their work clothes and passengers in their suits, ties, pantsuits. Two fat women were dishing out doughnuts and coffee with incredible efficiency, and the cash register rang like a record stuck in one spot. Doug bumped, bobbled, and spilled his way through the crowd until he spotted a table with some open seats.

"Over here, Mike," he yelled.

"Right, man."

"The *Canberra*," Doug said, seating himself.

"The *Canberra* what?" Mike asked.

"I don't know, just 'The *Canberra*.'"

"Man, are you drunk or something? First you don't like women, then you're talking to yourself. Very strange things."

"I didn't say anything about women. It's just that.... Forget it."

Mike sipped his coffee. "Man, you wouldn't believe the women on that ship. Michaels told me he laid one."

"That's his business. I don't give a shit."

"Hey, I'm your friend, remember? I'm Mike. I'm not mad at you. Don't get so goddam mad."

"I'm not mad at you. I'm sorry. It's just that. . . . I don't know any more."

"It's just what?'

Doug thought that Mike deserved whatever he told him. "All right, bastard! I don't even know if I can have intercourse any more without permanently impairing myself."

"What?" Mike paused to think if he really heard correctly. "What do you mean? Somebody cut your balls off?"

"They might just as well have. I've got this lousy disease. If I get real excited, my mind starts flashing and all kinds of things. I can get paralyzed, and I can't do a goddam thing about it. I can't do a thing. That's the bitch of it: I can't act."

Mike made his chair stand up on its two back legs. He tried to look at Doug's face, but it was bent over a coffee cup. Mike had ceaseless sounds of "Oh Shit" and "Goddam" running through his head, but he couldn't say those things, they were too defeating. He waited for Doug to look at him again. "I don't know what to say, man."

"It's all right," Doug said. "Like an oldtimer once told me, 'Just go your own way.' So do it."

"All right, all right! Look, I know you've got a hell of a thing, but OK, go your own way, ruin your whole asshole life. And I'll go my way, and everybody will go his way, and nobody will give a shit about anybody."

"Now wait. . . ."

"Goodbye!" Mike said. He hustled his coat on and stormed out the door.

Doug waited a few minutes before he left, watching his fingers twitch without any willful command.

Outside the restaurant, storm clouds were forming into great funnels over the bay, and a purple haze covered most of the city. Doug wondered if this was really happening or if it was just another hallucination. For all he knew, his mind might be flashing again, causing the sky to look this way. He thought that the sky and even the whole world might be flashing back at him, as if carrying out some insane, inverted plot to destroy him. This was what was happening, and it was now, he thought. It might be reality. It *was* reality, because, flashing or no flashing, this was what was happening. He felt himself caught up totally in the present, with no relating factors, with no more power over himself than over the weather, the water, the *Canberra*, the whole goddam universe. If any laws, codes, morals were to be formulated, they would have to be formulated from this point of time on.

His mind began rolling from one structure to another, to thoughts and to structures of thoughts, to water and wind and. . . .

As if the lightning threatening in the sky had suddenly decided to explode in his mind, he thought of the *Canberra* and the old man. The old man wanted to remember the ship that way, Doug thought, for just that moment of time, for that split second when the entire ship was showing itself, before it was cut off by the structure of the pier. He left then, and I stayed seeing only smaller and smaller portions of the ship, as if that could recall the entire thing.

The fifteen-minute warning whistle blew, and everyone bumped and bashed their way on board to make the departure time. The tugs made way alongside the *Canberra*. Everyone was waiting and throwing streamers and yelling to each other and taking pictures.

Finally, the ship backed out into the bay. This time there was no unexplainable silence. People were still waving, striving to be heard.

Doug was holding his head, trying to keep his brains from falling out.

"So Michaels got one of you!" he shouted. "Maybe I do give a shit. Pray, people! Loudly! To the God. To the God, people, who is the joy of MY youth."

When some longshoremen revived him, he was shaking all over, quivering back and forth, and straining at his roots like a mainsail in a big wind that threatens to crack the mast.

They told him he would be all right if he just took it easy. If he would just take it easy and relax, they told him, of course everything would be all right.

Frisco Blackie

He sat on
a farting forklift,
Shoulders content
to sag and shade
the beer belly bumping
the steering wheel
through two sweaters
and a one-button
peacoat.

A cold, fat cigar
brushed gray whiskers
as he chewed the end,
watching me.
One finger moved
off the wheel
and beckoned me
into the circle
of fumes.

I was here in '34
he said.
They call me
Frisco Blackie.
You're new
I can tell.
A cherry.
But that's all right.
What
do they call you?

Gene.

Not much to that
he said
lips laughing
eyes flashing.
But that's all right.
I used to be Pete
before the '34 Strike.

What happened
I asked
?

The Union
sent me to travel the coast
to organize.
Up North they'd call you
by where you was from.
That's the Frisco part.

And the
Blackie?

I could say
from the color of my hair
Now his throat was
laughing too
But it wasn't—
that came from
what I used
for an organizing
tool.

You mean
a blackjack?

All of him laughed
until he coughed
and choked
and pulled the
cigar
like a cork
out of his mouth
Filling the shed
with his sound.

Not so much
for the organizing—
the men were ready
back then—
More for protection
from the goon squads
an' such.

He jammed the
forklift into low
grating the gears
intentionally.

Been down here
almost fifty years
he said
And the only thing
I'll keep when
I leave is
my name.

He drove off
rumbling
bumping down
the dock
spewing blue clouds
behind him until
he was so far away
he and the forklift
began to wobble.

Leaving me to wonder
if
I'd ever get
to make a waterfront
name of my own.

I heard
years later
Blackie died
six months into
retirement.
It happened so sudden,
they said,
he forgot to take
that blackjack
laughter
with him.

The Expert

One time I won a ten-dollar bet from a second mate by telling a lie. But there are lies and lies—and my conscience never bothered me about that one. The longshore gang I was working in was loading baggage and ship stores aboard one of the American President Line passenger boats at Pier 50 in San Francisco. The cargo included trunks, suitcases, canned goods, the instruments of the ship's band, and cases of top-brand liquor. We longed to sample the Old Granddad but were foiled by a watchful storekeeper plus the second mate, who was supervising stowage.

The mate didn't say much except "Put it here" or "Put it there" until the musical instruments came aboard. Then he called out, "Now, be careful, men! Fragile cargo! Handle with care!" Somehow he seemed to be joking, chuckling and looking around as if he wanted to share the joke with someone. His eyes lit on me and my partner, Walter. He walked over, leaned close, and said, "Now, we don't want to damage those Jewboys' precious violins—now, do we? Why, they'd cry like babies." He put his finger alongside his nose in a waterfront gesture that means "We're in the know" and walked away.

We looked at each other. Walter shook his head in mock disbelief. "Did you get that? He's something."

I nodded. "He's probably one of those experts that can tell a Jew just by looking at him. You know the type, Walter."

"Yeah. And just because we're big, blond, and blue-eyed he thinks we're bigots like himself. I'm going to tell him off!"

I said, "Hold it. That's too easy. Let's figure out something—something that will cost him."

As we worked we plotted.

While waiting for the next load to come in, we approached the mate. Walter said, "So you've got an all-Jew band on this boat? What do they call themselves? The Hebes?"

The mate liked Walter's question. He laughed appreciatively and replied, "Of course not. Jewboys—Hebes as you call them—try not to give themselves away. But they can't fool me."

"I guess you can tell just by looking at them," I said.

"Sure can."

"I wish I could. Some of those musicians don't look like Jews to me."

The mate wagged a finger. "You've gotta learn to check out their noses and—especially—their close-set eyes." He lowered his voice. "Besides, everybody knows band musicians are either kikes or niggers, and there ain't any niggers in this bunch."

Walter broke in, "But just the same—you can tell them just by looking at them?"

"Never fail."

"Do you mind if we test you?" I asked.

"What do you mean?"

"Well, there happens to be one Jew in this gang. I bet you ten dollars you can't spot him."

"Ten dollars?" The mate's eyes narrowed suspiciously.

Walter smiled reassuringly. "What we really want is to see you in action. The bet just makes it more interesting. What's ten dollars?"

The mate turned and carefully scrutinized the other members of the gang. Tow-headed Sven; two blacks, Albert and Percy; two Italians, Joe and Gino; and Emile. Gino was nicknamed "Becco d'Aquila"—"Eaglebeak." Emile had a big nose too, but it wasn't in the same class with Gino's. And I don't remember if anybody in the gang had close-set eyes.

The mate completed his survey and turned back to us, smiling confidently. "I'll take that bet."

"You spotted him already?" asked Walter. "But first shell out, both of you. I'll hold the money."

I asked, "OK, who's the Jew?"

The mate replied, "You thought I'd pick that guy, didn't you?" He indicated "Eaglebeak." "But I heard his partner call him Gino. He's a Wop." He paused, then pointed at Emile "That's the Jew, that dark one sitting on the trunk."

Now we struck for the jugular. Walter yelled, "Hey, Emile! Are you a Jew?"

Emile stood up. "Who sez so?"

Walter held up a cautioning hand. "Now take it easy, Emile. We got a bet with the mate, that's all. Just answer yes or no. Are you a Jew?"

"You damn fool. You know I'm a Syrian!"

Walter didn't hesitate. He passed the twenty over to me.

The mate was plenty upset. "Why did you have to yell it out like that? You know, I think you guys tricked me. There's no Jew in this gang."

I put the twenty into my wallet, pulled out my waterfront security pass and pointed, "My name is Asher—one of the twelve tribes of Israel—and Harer, a name as Jewish as they come. I'm the Jew."

The mate stared at me with genuine hatred. Walter broke it up with a shout. "Hey, guys! The drinks are on Asher tonight. He just won ten dollars from the mate. The mate bet Emile was a Jew!"

"No!"

"Yeah!"

Then Albert got into the act. "Hey, Mister Mate. Why didn't you bet on me and Percy? We're Jews from Texas—got a little sunburned, that's all." He slapped Percy on the back and laughed uproariously. Everybody joined in. The mate couldn't take it. He made for the nearest companionway and disappeared.

Walter said, "Good riddance. Now maybe I can liberate a bottle of that Old Granddad. But seriously, Asher. Do you think we taught him a lesson?"

"I don't know. Right now I only know one thing—that I've never been so glad that my German-Cherokee father and my Swedish-English mother gave me a Jewish name."

Up Top

I became Master of the Sea
one September night
when me and Steve were topmen
aboard a Matson van ship at Seventh Street.

The sun was trying to set
when the shift began,
pushing hard against magenta pillows
that billowed above the water.

We volunteered to go topside
to be alone with a bottle of brandy
some fine Colombian

(And escape
   the furrowed frustration of working below,
(Trying to follow
   the programmed
   lashing pattern
   without cracking
   knuckle or knee
   in the cramped catwalk
   between tiers
   of metallic tombs
(Where lubricated
   lashing gear
   coats gloves
   and coveralls
   with layers of grease,
(Weatherproofed
   against rain, sweat,
   and torrents of tedium,
(Where there's
   nowhere
   to hide
   from the pursuit
   of a superintendent's
   pressuring gaze).

Delivered up top as hard-hat cowboys,
riding the crane bridle a hundred feet high,
Ready to get loaded down
before the midnight lunch hour.

Vans stacked symmetrically
four high on deck, ready for discharge.
Tightroping the edge,
bending to release lashing cables,
watching them whip and snake
and clunk to the deck below.
Brandy chased the weedsmoke down
and tuned the night too clear
for daytime stoned-out eyes.

I stand astride a container
Pissing offshore into the wind,
arcing yellow eighty feet down
into the bilgewater of the Bay.

The crane broke down
when the sun was gone,
turned sideways, and plucked
buckets of black blood
out of the sky.

We sit offshore,
legs dangling,
waiting for stilts
to walk across the water;
Suck final fumes
from the bottle,
take a terminal toke,
and hover above the
undulating line of lights
on the Bay Bridge,
race star shadows
under the Golden Gate,
And guide ships
through safe channels
to slumber harbor in my Bay.

SILVA

The Commute

This morning
on the way to work
I raced a red dawn west
across the bay
to San Francisco.

I half wanted to lose,
to feel the warm
against my back
before reaching
the fog bank finish line.

My feet
were already warm,
snuggled deep
in double socks to
withstand a day of cold
unloading frozen lamb
and veal from New Zealand.

I shivered
at the picture
of icebound chunks packed
perfectly
in the most solid
stuck-together 50-lb. boxes
ever to shatter shins
and frosted fingers.

Just the other side
of Treasure Island,
where
the soul of the city begins,
A magic moment stopped
the Ferry Building clock:

I discovered
your smell
was still
on my hands,
filling my mind
with you,
last night:

A panther trapped
in a pulsating prism,
Supple sounds resonating,
reverberating,
at the purple end
of the spectrum.

It seems
I'm no good
at painting nightmares
any more.

Of Friends and Factions

Scouts from splinter groups
scurry like termites
in front of the Friday pay window,
Fulfilling an historical mission
proselytizing the longshore division
of the working working class.

So many good comrades busy
charting a course to redemption,
No time to look up
and lose the squint they've
acquired from pondering
political blueprints.

Creatures of the world of Ist
and Ism hawking tabloids penned
in the purity of 1905,
telling me the error of my ways
without knowing my name;
Seeking recruits
for the secretarial pool
of someone else's wordy
revolution.

I've already received
enough dictation for
one lifetime, so
Paint your slogans
on Someone Else's eyes.

In the Hold

Fade in on a series of sepia-toned still photographs the size of the screen itself, of the general strike of 1934 in San Francisco. They click by as methodically as police mug shots, in silence:

☐ A cordon of mounted police along the San Francisco waterfront, blocking access to the piers

☐ Long lines of angry, shouting longshoremen, gesturing and shaking clenched fists

☐ Thousands of spectators on the hills above the waterfront, below Coit Tower, sitting on the grass, waiting for the battle to begin

☐ Battle scenes of police in gas masks charging into the striking longshoremen, beating them with clubs, firing their pistols at random, throwing tear gas

☐ A battle scene of longshoremen choking on tear gas, retreating, throwing bricks, rocks, pulling mounted policemen from their horses

☐ A heroic young longshoreman in his early twenties shouting a cry of some sort to his fellow strikers

☐ The bodies of two dead longshoremen lying on the cobblestone streets in pools of blood

☐ A second photograph of the same young longshoreman, holding the head of one of the dead men in his lap

☐ A massive funeral cortege along the waterfront with thousands following it, the streets lined with solemn spectators, hats in their hands.

As the last picture clicks past, the SCREEN GOES COMPLETELY DARK.

In the lower left-hand corner of the screen the words "San Francisco Waterfront, 1970" appear.

Holding the Darkness, we Dissolve thru to:

Interior: the Hold of a Ship

Sound of distant, MUFFLED VOICES, the TRAMP OF FEET. At the top of the darkened screen, several thin rays of light suddenly stream downward through the cracks in the hatch boards.

A rat, sitting on its haunches, munches a piece of refuse, profiled slightly by the light from above.

As one of the hatch boards is lifted up, we get a GLIMPSE of the face of a longshoreman framed by a patch of blue sky.

A second longshoreman is SEEN, another hatch board is lifted aside.

Exterior: the Deck of the Ship—Morning

From HIGH UP we are LOOKING FORE AND AFT to SEE the longshoremen swarming over the ship, rigging gear, uncovering the hatches, etc. It is just past eight o'clock, and the men turn to with a boisterous spirit, singing, whistling, hammering at themselves with goodnatured profanity.

At Hatch 4 Charley Bucksmith directs his gang. He's a bearded giant of a man, middle-aged, weathered, with a crazy look in his eye. Around him at various places on deck are two WINCH DRIVERS and six HOLDMEN. Generally, the holdmen are young, anywhere from their twenties to their early forties. The guys on the winches are oldtimers like Charley.

The yard boom, the one nearest the dock, is being pulled by hand out over the dock.

Charley's eyes are constantly aloft. He shouts and swears with exaggerated, intimidating intent.

Charley: Slack the fuckin' mid-ship guy! You—the cherry with the ponytail! Shake hands with the goddamn preventer chain, will ya?

A young hippie, hair tied back, gawks over his shoulder at Charley, cowed by his presence. He pulls awkwardly on a heavy, grease-covered chain.

Charley (Off stage): That's a good girl. Careful ya don't get yer fuckin' hands dirty! Awright, get the boom out, for Christ's sake!

Charley wears an old, battered tweed coat and a filthy fedora hat. He moves across the deck to the railing and looks down at the dock.

There are men at work everywhere you look. Forklifts weave in and out of the shed bringing various kinds of gear alongside the ship. Again, the sounds of the dock match those on deck — profane, happy, musical.

Charley glances up at the boom, takes out a pint bottle of whiskey from his coat pocket and pulls on it, then looks off toward the city skyline to see a seagull swoop down out of the fog. He calls out to the dock:

Charley: Hey Julie, spot the boom for me, will ya?

Exterior: the Dock

Julie Shannon leans against the shed, hands in his pockets. He is the same man we saw in the still photographs, cradling the head of a dead longshoreman in his arms. He's a brawny, rough-looking man in his early fifties now, dressed in the classic San Francisco longshoreman's style of faded black 'Frisco jeans, striped hickory shirt, and a soiled white cap pulled down over one ear. He's cut from pure workingclass cloth; it's written all over him, and he wears it like some long-forgotten badge.

But there's more to him when you look closer, much more. A gentle, intelligent expression in the eyes, a look of worn courage, a scarred, embattled sensitivity beneath the deeply weathered workman's face. The CAMERA MOVES WITH him as he walks out to the middle of the dock, eyes on the boom above him. He stands directly underneath it so that he can measure the distance from where the hook will hang to the edge of the dock, trying to center the boom in the most advantageous place.

Julie (to Charley): You gotta come down, Charley, you're too close to the ship. Lower your boom some, babe.

Above, Charley nods, then disappears.

Exterior: on Deck

The Hippie and his partner, a YOUNG BLACK MAN, are clumsily trying to lower the boom up on the bridge by the winches. Charley climbs up, swearing loudly.

Charley (shoving the Hippie aside): No, no, not that way, dummy! Over the top! Look out!

Hippie: Well, Jesus, can't you at least show me how?

Charley looks him over, dumbfounded.

Charley (in a booming voice, laughing): Jesus Christ, I don't know whether to *fire* ya or *fuck* ya!

Laughter from all angles—then Charley shows them how it's done, CAMERA TIGHT on him as he takes the wire rope over the top of the drum, then signals the winch driver, who lowers the boom down over the dock to a better position.

Exterior: the Dock—Later

Shannon and his partner, Bartholomew Jones, are sitting on a stack of pallet boards. Jones is near retirement age, a black man with close-cropped, fleecy hair, and a worn, kindly air. He is smoking a cigar and musing about something as he stares down at his feet.

Shannon's face is completely hidden behind a copy of the *Wall Street Journal.*

Bart glances at him a couple of times as if to get his attention.

Bart: Payday, ain't it? (*beat*) Reckon I'll lay me some pipe t'night.

Shannon grunts but does not lower the paper.

Julie: Your pipe-layin' days been over for a long time, pal.

Bart (chuckling): Least I *think* about doin' it. I don't be settin' 'round readin' no *Wall Street Ju'nul.* (*slaps Shannon's leg)* Load comin' out.

Pulling on their gloves they move slowly across the dock toward the ship, their eyes on the load of cargo as it descends.

Julie: Listen, Bart, the only way you can find what is *really* happening in this country is by readin' the *Wall Street Journal*. They give you the *real* skinny.

Above them, at the railing, the second winch driver, who is tending hatch, uses hand signals to bring the load down slowly onto the dock, stopping a few inches above the ground so that Shannon and Bart can steady it before landing it. The falls are loosened, the bridle goes slack, and they unhook the load.

Julie: You watch what the money people are doin', you find out what's goin' on, Bart.

The empty hook sails up and out of sight and they amble back toward their positions on the pallet boards. Bart chuckles to himself.

Bart: You 'posed to be an old revolutionary, not some cap'list worryin' 'bout his money.

Shannon glances sharply at him, but he says nothing. As he moves back to his seat a shadow seems to fall across his face.

Another OLDTIMER has taken his place behind the Wall Street Journal. All we can SEE are two big, gnarled hands.

Oldtimer: Son-of-a-bitch.

Bart: What's wrong, baby?

Oldtimer: Fuckin' market's fallin' apart. IT&T dropped eight points.

He lowers the paper and looks at Bart and Shannon as though he has been betrayed. He has a battered face, a twisted nose, three days' growth of beard, and the look of a Skid Row bum.

Oldtimer (in a rasping voice): What the hell's goin' on out there, Julie? I can't figure out what to tell my fuckin' broker.

Julie: Beats me, Frank. Better watch the game, though.

Nearby, leaning against the side of the shed, is MICHAEL, a young, bearded man with a studious, revolutionary look. He wears a Greek fisherman's cap and wire, rimless glasses. He has been watching Bart, Shannon and the Oldtimer.

Exterior: the Dock—Later

The CAMERA PANS SLOWLY DOWN the length of the ship, MOVING PAST successive pairs of hook-on men, most of whom, but by no means all, are oldtimers, sitting quietly or chatting in the late morning sun between loads; we catch GLIMPSES of the *Racing Form*, the *People's Daily Worker*, the *Rolling Stone*, the *New York Review of Books*, etc. Forklifts flow back and forth, and the endless talk sessions go on. Clearly, we are in a private world.

Exterior: on Deck of the Ship

A WALKING BOSS — or foreman — in a white hard hat peers down into the hold.

Walking Boss (angrily): I don't give a damn if there's a fuckin' grizzly bear down there! Just keep pumpin'!

Far, far down into the hold we SEE a LONGSHOREMAN standing in the square of the hatch holding a rat up by the tail.

Longshoreman: You get the mate down here! We ain't workin' with rats in the hold! That shit went out in the fuckin' nineteenth century!

From beneath the wings of the hatch we HEAR a scattered CHORUS of: "Yeah, that shit went out with the nineteenth century."

Exasperated, the Walking Boss takes his hard hat off, rubs his head.

Walking Boss: All right, I'll get the mate! But keep the hook movin', ya hear?

He leaves.

Down below, several faces pop out from the wings.

Same Longshoreman: It says in the contract we do not have to work with beasts of prey!

Howls of laughter.

Interior: the Shed

A group of MEN — a mixture of black, white, and Mexican — are on an afternoon coffee break, lounging on some piled cargo. A heated discussion is taking place and at the center of it is RICK McTEIRNAN, a gray-bearded oldtimer.

McTeirnan: I'm telling you, fellas, the Nine Point Four Three clause will kill us if we don't do something about it. It's a violation of everything we fought for in the '34 strike.

Off to one side, Julie Shannon sits on a pile of coffee sacks. He's reading a book and his detachment from the group is striking.

Carlos (heavy Mexican accent): C'mon, McTeirnan. Don't get so carried away, man. All the companies want is the right to hire a few steady guys to work the new equipment. What is the matter with you, bringing up this shit about the '34 strike? Always the goddamn '34 strike. I get tired of hearing about that shit. This is 1970 man. It's a different world.

Pete, a light-skinned black who wears a necktie with his work shirt, is next.

Pete: Lose ya freedom ya fucked, baby. Same old world, then.

At this Shannon's ears pick up sharply, and he begins to eavesdrop, without looking up from his reading.

McTeirnan: Right on, Charley. How many you guys have read the contract?

Tommie (an older black): I ain't read the sum-bitch.

Richards: Do it say in the nine point four three the Man can on'y have jus' so many steady-mens?

Michael (off stage, incredulous): I can't *believe* this! You mean you men haven't read the *contract*?! Hell, it expires in a month!

Heads turn to look at Michael, standing on the edge of the circle. They study him briefly — as does Shannon in the b.g.

McTeirnan whips out the contract — a small pocket-sized, vinyl-covered book — and opens it on a dog-eared page.

McTeirnan (reading): Here it is. Listen to this: "The employers shall be entitled to hire steady, skilled equipment operators—*without limit as to numbers or length* of time in steady employment." See what I mean?

Tony, a gray-haired, cigar-smoking Italian with a contemplative air, joins in.

Tony: No.

McTeirnan: If this is carried to an extreme, they won't need a hiring hall.

Michael (breaking in): Exactly! Once they start hiring a few steady-men they've got their foot in the door. They can drive a wedge right through the union!

Carlos (angrily): You guys are fucking shit-disturbers! There is no way we could ever lose the hiring hall!

McTeirnan (patiently): Carlos, don't kid yourself. Sure, we're gettin' fat now with all this Vietnam cargo. But what about later, when times get lean? A lot of the guys will take the steady jobs to get the pork chops, see? (He throws a glance toward Shannon) There's a guy who knows. Ask him.

They turn and look toward Shannon, who continues reading.

McTeirnan: Hey, Julie—why don't you start coming to the meetings again? Hit the microphone like in the old days. We could sure use you on this steady-man issue.

Shannon closes the book, slides down off the coffee sacks, and gives them an emphatic thumbs-down gesture. Then he walks away.

Michael hurries after him, the CAMERA TRACKING him out to the dock. As Shannon starts to sit down on the pallet boards, Michael taps him on the shoulder.

Michael: You're Shannon, right?

Julie: Yeah. So what?

Michael: Why'd you walk away?

Shannon looks him over.

Julie: That any of your business?

Michael: Yes, it is.

Shannon takes off his cap, runs his hand through his hair and sighs wearily.

Bart appears from the shed and sits down. Their coffee break is over.

Michael: I don't get it. What's *wrong* with you oldtimers? The steady-man issue is explosive. It's going to create a class struggle within the union and possibly destroy the concept of trade unionism.

Julie: Oh, yeah. . . .

Bart and Julie get up to move toward a load coming out of the hatch. Michael follows them out to the hook.

Michael: Every oldtimer I talk to is more concerned with the Dow-Jones Average, or how much rent he's collecting on his spec property, or the price of a new camper. It's shocking as hell!

They land the load, and the forklift driver takes it away. Michael follows them back to the palletboards.

Michael: I mean . . . like you're supposed to be an old militant leader. What are you doing now? Why have all you guys withdrawn? Why all the apathy?

Shannon looks amused by the tirade.

Bart: What's apathy?

Julie: That's when you get a splinter in your ass and you're too lazy to take it out. Like you.

Michael: You don't know what it's like in the hold now. The employer is fucking us over on manning, safety, all kinds of things— and nobody gives a shit! All I see around me are a bunch of pie-carders!

The term "pie-carder" is a bad word in union parlance — and Shannon reacts to it immediately; but before he can we HEAR an awful CRY OF PAIN further down the dock. Shannon starts to move, then, jaw muscles flexing, thrusts his face close to Michael's.

Julie (low): Listen, lad, just remember one thing . . . (*jabs him in the chest with one finger*) When you got here the table was already set. Don't forget it.

Shannon breaks down the dock; Michael starts to follow him.

Michael: Don't give me that old cliché!

Julie: Take a hike, will you? We got an injured man down here!

A HOOK-ON MAN, one of the younger ones, is bent double, one hand clutching the other at his crotch, his face twisted in pain.

As the load swings up and away we can SEE a glove caught in the wire sling, mashed against the load.

Several men rush to the injured man's side, Shannon among them.

Interior: the Hold—Day

As the load is landed in the square – or center – of the hatch, a LONGSHORE-MAN notices the glove. The load is unhooked and the man feels inside the glove, then quickly withdraws his hand. He glances up at the Winch Driver.

Longshoreman: Hey, Bobbie! Come on back with the hook! I got some guy's finger here!

The Winch Driver comes back with the empty bridle. The other men gather around, put the glove on a pallet board, and send it out.

Exterior: the Dock—Same Time

The injured man, holding his hand, a sick look on his face. Next to him is a Walking Boss, taking down his statement.

A LONGSHOREMAN rushes over and hands the injured man his glove; a crowd gathers around. He shakes the glove and the tip of his little finger drops out.

Longshoreman: Hey, Paul, they sent your finger back out!

Paul (furious): Dumb motherfuckers!

Julie (calmly): Take the finger to the hospital. Maybe they can graft it back on. I've seen it happen.

Off stage there is a ROAR of MANIACAL LAUGHTER.

Exterior: on Deck

Charley Bucksmith, leaning against the railing, watches the scene below. He cups his hand around his mouth and shouts down to the dock.

Charley: Talk about givin' a man the finger!

Cut to:

Exterior: the Fairmont Hotel—Day

Tom Kincaid steps out of a cab. He is a sharply dressed, street-wise, tough-looking man in his late thirties. He pays the driver, beckons for a porter for his luggage, enters the famous old hotel.

Transitional Action Excerpted from Play

Shannon's wife, Lydia, teaches music at a conservatory in Oakland. She's a lively, radiant woman, with a kind of Sierra Club look about her, very physical and open. She comes from a large, wealthy, liberal East Coast family, and her aristocratic appearance is at intriguing odds with Julie's diamond-in-the-rough, proletarian look. Lydia is a veteran of assorted liberal and/or radical causes over the years; even now, her "liberal" 1967 Volvo is plastered with a variety of ragged bumper stickers having to do with Vietnam and other matters of late 1960's concern.

When she arrives home that night she finds her husband slumped in his chair in front of the television set watching scenes of Vietnam carnage with the sound off. As always, this alarms her, and she moves quickly to distract him. She has brought home a ton of literature on New Zealand, where they plan to go later that summer on a back-packing trip. While sitting on his lap, she carries on a spirited, playful dialogue with him about their plans. He listens half-heartedly, one eye on the telly, but he's so obviously susceptible to her charm that his mood lightens quickly. We get the feeling they're carrying on a lifelong affair.

She then makes the mistake of interrupting things to read him a letter from their son that has arrived that morning. He is with the Colorado Forestry Service. Listening, we can tell that son Charlie is not exactly a chip off the old revolutionary block. He writes glowingly of how lucky he thinks he is to be in a remote spot in the wilderness "away from the peace marches and the riots and all that militant crap." *All that militant crap?* Julie thinks. Christ—my own kid.

The next morning, as Julie starts out the door on his way to work, he lifts an old, rusted cargo hook down from the coat rack and sticks it in his pocket. Watching him, Lydia thinks: Another omen; they're coming faster: he hasn't carried a hook since he quit the hold fifteen years ago. She kisses him and reminds him that they're going to a reunion of the Abraham Lincoln Brigade that night.

At the same time, Tom Kincaid is checking into the Fairmont Hotel. Tom is the son of Johnnie Kincaid, who was Julie Shannon's closest friend. They fought together in the Spanish Civil War. Johnnie was killed there, in fact he died in Julie's arms, leaving behind four children and a wife who never really understood what the war was all about and who grew to loathe the memory of it and all other left-wing causes—an obsession she passed on to at least one of her children.

Tom Kincaid is now thirty-two, a hooded man—a loner. He makes his living as a kind of trouble-shooter for corporate interests in labor-management struggles. His specialty is busting up or undermining or in any way harassing unions to the benefit of his employer of the moment, and the more militant the union the better he likes his work. He's a gunfighter—in town to take on the longshore union. The shipowners want to finish automating the waterfront, and union resistance in certain areas is giving them trouble—and costing them money.

At a meeting that morning, Kincaid listens impatiently to the shipowners' suggestions, which he finds academic and unrealistic. He's done his homework—are they ready to listen now? He takes out a copy of the contract and reads the 9.43 clause, the steady-man issue. "Hit them there," he says bluntly. "It's a loaded gun. Use 9.43 to drive a wedge in the union, disrupt the hiring hall and try to break down the spirit of militancy San Francisco longshoremen are noted for. Exploit this issue to the hilt, and don't be afraid to spend lots of bread doing it. You guys are getting fat off this war, same as the men."

After the meeting, he stands by the window and looks down on the waterfront six stories below: ships as far as he can see. He suddenly thinks of Julie Shannon—and of his father. Would Shannon recognize him? he wonders. Not that it matters. If it hadn't been for Shannon maybe his old man'd still be alive. Then it occurs to him that maybe Shannon is still active in union affairs, maybe their paths will cross; he'd love nothing better than to take him on, head to head. But then again maybe he's like so many other old lefties, withdrawn, no fight left in him.

On the docks below, Shannon sits and broods over his life, wondering the same thing.

The action now resumes.

Exterior: a Parking Lot—Oakland Waterfront—Night

The Shannons park their car and get out. Julie looks himself over, smooths down his hair.

Julie: How do I look—OK?

Lydia looks him over: at his dated, wide-bottomed trousers, a sports coat that is a size too small, a blue work shirt, and a tie that is badly off center.

Lydia (biting her lip): Fabulous.

They walk into the restaurant, a fishhouse specializing in banquets and large parties.

Interior: the Restaurant

A banner is spread across the entrance to one of the banquet rooms: "Welcome Veterans of the Abraham Lincoln Brigade — 32nd Anniversary."

The CAMERA ROAMS THROUGH the lobby and INTO the bar where many of the guests are milling about. We are LOOKING AT a group of middle-aged people of mixed appearance and status. There are distinguished professional-looking men with their handsomely dressed wives, and there are working class couples of humbler style.

All mingle together freely, there is a lot of embracing, squeals of delight and warm handshaking, and faces everywhere wreathed in wide smiles.

The Shannons enter and pause to look around. There is a momentary lull in the swing of things as people notice them standing side by side in what is a kind of accidental portrait: Lydia beautiful, nonchalant, poised; Julie self-conscious, yet dignified.

Then a number of people rush to greet them, and they become separated, Julie slipping from one embrace to another as he greets old comrades.

Interior: a Banquet Room

Robin Smith, a woman Lydia's age, embraces her. Robin is well-tailored, handsome, bursting with a career woman's vitality.

Robin: I'm sorry I didn't get back to you yesterday. I had a long deposition.

Lydia: That's OK. Maybe we'll get a chance to talk tonight. Come on—Julie would love to see you.

Interior: a Banquet Room

The guests have long since finished dinner; smoke hangs thick in the air, as do the endless speeches.

Voice (off stage): . . . for the unrelenting criticism of the moral corruption, intellectual stupefaction, and spiritual degradation that are disseminated for mass consumption through the dominant culture and . . .

As the VOICE FADES, the CAMERA PANS ALONG one of the long tables and CENTERS on Lydia and Julie Shannon and Robin Smith. APPLAUSE as the speaker finishes. Julie looks uncomfortable.

Stretched above the speaker's dais is a banner that reads "Madrid Next Year!!" The MASTER OF CEREMONIES (M.C.) takes the mike.

M.C.: I would like now to read a few telegrams that have been pouring in. "Though I greet my valiant comrades of the Abraham Lincoln Brigade from distant Moscow, my heart is with you on this day and all days. Death to fascism! Death to the butcher, Franco! I celebrate this anniversary with the sure knowledge that I shall soon embrace you all in Madrid." Signed "La Pasionaria!"

A spontaneous BURST OF APPLAUSE greets this, and a chorus of "Viva La Pasionaria! Viva La Pasionaria!"

M.C. (reading another telegram): "There is a great need today for the spirit of internationalism that moved members of the Brigade to stand shoulder to shoulder with their Spanish brothers and sisters in a great civil war. That spirit of courage and self-sacrifice shown in the face of the fascist monster should serve as an example for those today who still face the beast in Spain, in Portugal, in the Middle East, and in Southeast Asia. For the reactionary forces that have enchained . . . "

Julie stares into his empty coffee cup. Suddenly he whispers something in Lydia's ear, slides his chair back and leaves the table.

Interior: the Bar

Julie stands alone at the service bar with a drink in his hand, looking distraught. The BARTENDER drifts down to make conversation.

Bartender: Taking a break?

Julie: Yeah. You wanna do this again?

He shoves his glass toward the Bartender and watches him pour.

Suddenly from down the bar we HEAR a BOOMING VOICE.

Booming Voice (off stage): The problem is to hammer out a revolutionary line that vill bring the working class into the mainstream of American life!

Julie looks down and sees a powerfully built, retired longshoreman named Gunnar, holding forth with some younger men.

Gunnar: Ve must take a positive position as Commanists even in the most got-damn reactionary unions. But, comrades, listen, our base must be broad! No more of the sectarianism that plagued our movement in the past!

He smashes his huge fist down on the bar.

Gunnar: Ve must *not* become isolated from the American mainstream!

Julie smiles and shakes his head.

A Younger Man (to Gunnar): But you do agree that somehow Meany has to be stripped before the working class as a stalking horse of reactionarism?

Julie drains his glass and leaves.

Just as he starts to enter the banquet room again he hears the STRAINS of an old Spanish Civil War fight song.

Interior: the Room

All of the guests are on their feet, singing.

Voices:

> 'Freiheit!
> Far off is our land
> Yet ready we stand
> We're fighting and winning for you
> Freiheit!
> Spanish heavens spread their
>   brilliant light
> High above our trenches in the plain
> From the distance morning comes to
>   greet us ... '

Lydia and Robin Smith sing out loud and clear, nostalgia flooding their faces . . .

The Voices:

'We'll not yield a foot to
    Franco's Fascists,
Even though the bullets fall
    like sleet
With us stand ... '

Julie stands inside the doorway, feeling the emotion welling up inside him. His lips move to the words, his voice barely audible.

Julie: 'Beat the drums. Ready bayonets, charge! Forward march! Victory our reward!'

Face twisted in sudden despair he lowers his head, rubs his hand across his eyes as the song ends with tremendous APPLAUSE, CHEERS, etc.

Dissolve to:

Interior: the Shannons' Car—Night

Lydia is driving, Julie is slumped down beside her; he's a bit smashed and there's a sullenness to his silence. She pulls up to the toll plaza, pays the bridge crossing, and they start across the Oakland Bay Bridge.

Lydia is happy, filled with pleasant thoughts about the evening; she sighs contentedly.

Lydia: God, it was great to see everyone again. Can you believe how good George and Berte look? They haven't aged at all. I wonder how we looked to them . . .

She glances across at him, then lays a hand on his leg.

Lydia (gently): Hey. I'm talking to you. (*beat*) Are you down? I mean—did it make you sad, seeing all those old faces?

Julie: No. Not a bit.

Lydia: I saw you talking to Billy Walker. I hear he's big in real estate now.

Julie: Yeah. He always was a champagne Communist.

Lydia throws him a glance.

Lydia: What the hell's eating you?

Julie (sighs): I don't know. . . . The whole thing didn't sit right. They all act like it happened yesterday. Same old speeches, same old clichés.

Lydia: What did you expect?—it was a reunion.

Julie: They'll never get that bastard Franco out. When he packs in, Prince what's-his-name will take over and it'll be more of the same.

Lydia is upset by the sudden bitterness in his voice.

Julie: You'd think they'd find a new cause . . . There's plenty of 'em around.

Lydia (coldly): Working for democracy in Spain is a perfectly good cause.

Julie (as if he hasn't heard): They're all so goddamned involved with the past.

Lydia: Naturally. It was that kind of war. They're marked by it. So are we.

Julie: Ah—I'm tired of livin' with the past.

The lights of the city appear ahead.

Cut to:

Interior: the Shannon Flat

Lydia stands against the kitchen sink, arms folded. She's obviously disturbed. There is an air of tension in the kitchen.

Julie reaches up to take down a bottle of brandy.

Julie: You want a nightcap?

Lydia: No, thanks . . . yes, I do. I'll have one.

He pours them each a snifter.

Lydia (an edgy sarcasm): I wasn't aware you were "living in the past." I thought we were rather enjoying the present.

Julie: You know what I mean. It's just that . . . well, it's all so predictable. Everything is laid out for us. You teach music, I sit on my ass all day on the dock like some goddamned relic, the house is paid for, we own property, we got money in the bank, we're safe. We're so fuckin' *safe.*

Lydia (a quiet anger): We have a right to be safe. We have earned the fucking right to be safe. Considering what we've been through.

Julie: Maybe so. But I can't . . . I can't seem to hack it.

He paces slowly about the kitchen, his face drawn.

Lydia studies him closely; she feels panic rising inside her.

Lydia: What are you doing, Julie? What are you thinking about?

He looks at her.

Julie: I don't know exactly. For one thing, I've been thinkin' of goin' back in the hold.

She gasps.

Lydia: You wouldn't dare!

Julie is taken off guard by her reaction.

Julie: I said I was just *thinkin'* about it. But anyway, why so surprised?

Lydia: *Why?* Oh, I don't know. Let's see if I can think up a few reasons. You're fifty-two years old, you spent twenty years in the hold, you have had broken ribs, stitches in your head, busted fingers, a bad back, and arthritis in one hand to show for it. And what else . . . oh, yes, how many men have been killed so far this year? Eleven, right? What did they die from—hay fever? . . . What other reasons can I give you? Surely I can think of a few more.

She glares angrily at him.

Lydia: Because you don't *belong* in the hold, that's why!

Julie: Where *do* I belong, Lydia? On a mountain top in New Zealand? That's where you got Harry—on a mountain in Colorado, a million miles from trouble, away from "all the crap," as he puts it. That's the way he said it, right?

Lydia (furiously): You leave Harry out of this! We've been through that before, damn it! Harry is a child of the Left, he's on neutral ground exactly where he wants to be!

Julie (shouting): And that's exactly where I *don't* want to be!

They glare at each other.

Julie: I'm goin' back in the hold. If nothin' else, I could use the exercise.

Lydia: You do and I'll leave, I swear it. Damn it, it's my life, too! I want you all in one piece. It's been twelve years since you quit the hold, and in all that time things have been peaceful. Or "safe," as you put it. No more FBI agents knocking on our doors, no jails, no injuries, no fights, no legal fees, no troubles. And I love it!

Julie (stunned): Enough to *leave* me?

She looks at him; she's bluffing but we can tell she's going to hang with it.

Lydia: Yes.

Julie: I don't believe this—

Lydia (on the verge of tears): —God *damn* it, why do you have to feel so responsible to the waterfront!

Julie (incredulous): Who said anything about being responsible? All I want is—

Lydia: —You know goddamn well what I mean! You're not going back for the exercise and you know it! You smell something, you sense some trouble brewing or whatever, I know you!

She starts to leave, then turns and fixes him with a blazing look.

Lydia (low): You can count me out. I've had enough of it.

She leaves him standing, mouth open, confused as hell.

Dissolve to:

Interior: the Shannon Bedroom—Dawn

The CAMERA IS TIGHT on Julie as we HEAR the ALARM GO OFF. The time is 5:45 AM. For a moment he doesn't move, as if afraid to; then he rises and drops his feet onto the floor.

He looks over his shoulder at Lydia's side of the bed; it's unslept in.

Interior: the Shannon Flat—Later

Julie, dressed now for work, starts out the door; he hesitates, reaches up on the coat rack and takes down the old cargo hook we saw earlier and shoves it into his back pocket.

Cut to:

Interior: Longshoremen's Hiring Hall—Day

An EXPLOSION OF NOISE, a thousand or more men all talking at the same time, standing around in clusters of five or six or more, chewing the fat. Some sit on chairs reading the morning papers, others push in against the bulletin boards to look for their dispatch numbers on long sheets. It's a bewildering array of humanity, a true melting pot: Mexicans, Spaniards, Basques, Irishmen, Chinese, Japanese, Hawaiians, Maltese, an equal and predominant number of black and white Americans, and over the NOISE and DIN we HEAR the steady DRONE of the Dispatcher's VOICE, calling out the numbers.

The dispatch office is an all-glass, two-tiered structure with a circular staircase in the middle. There's a lot of feverish activity on both levels by men in white shirts, pockets bulging with pencils.

On the lower level, we SEE a huge, bald BLACK MAN, the DISPATCHER, who intones in a deep, Paul Robeson-like bass, very slow, his eyes on a long sheet of paper.

Dispatcher: Sixty-five foughty-two, seb'nty-nine thirty-two, sixty-one twenty, down to a huner't an' eighteen hours . . . now I don' want to see *no* brother jumpin' the gun like yesterday, ya hear? 'Cause I be floppin' yo ass you do. We got plenty a woik this mornin', plenty of woik . . .

Shannon stands just inside the front door, eyes wide: he has forgotten what it was like! He takes his hat off, runs his hand through his hair, then flops the hat back on the side of his head and starts moving through the crowd.

Men reach out to shake his hand or slap him on the back.

We SEE three sets of iron railings, like chutes, leading to the three dispatch windows. There is only a small opening to speak through.

Longshoreman (to the Dispatcher): What'cha got this side, babe?

Dispatcher: Got freezer at 80, hides at 50B, coffee at 19.

Longshoreman: Fuck the coffee! Gimme some gravy. Ya got units there at 27? Yeah, gimme that—no, wait a min—

Dispatcher: Goddamn, man, I ain't got all mornin', let's go!

Longshoreman: Gimme 27, Pier 27!

Shannon's turn is next. He leans into the window.

Dispatcher: Hey, Big Julie! What the hell you doin' in the hold window, oldtimer? Shit, I thought you'd retired by now!

Julie: Got a ways to go yet, Pete. Gimme some hand-jive, anything you got. Yeah, I'll take coffee at 19. See if I can handle it.

Dispatcher: Your number?

Julie: 3636.

Dispatcher: There you go, pardner!

Shannon takes the job ticket and moves through the crowd toward the door.

Exterior: Pier 19—Day

There are maybe a hundred longshoremen milling about waiting for the signal to go to work. The tone is that of a fight crowd waiting around before the main event.

Shannon hands his job ticket to a GANG BOSS, an oldtimer about his own age.

Gang Boss: Hey, what's doin', Big Julie? You back in the hold?

VAWTER

Julie: How are you, Montana? Yeah, thought I'd give it a whirl.

Montana: Okay—we're in Hatch Number four aft. Gear's already rigged.

Interior: the Lunch Room

A dingy room inside the pier with several battered lunch tables. A couple of card games are underway. A clock on the wall reads "7:50." Bart Jones is playing in one of the games.

Julie walks in, goes over and stands behind Bart; leans down to kibbitz on his hand. Bart looks up, jerks his hand away as if he's mad, but he's only faking it.

Bart: Get out'a my face, I ain't talkin' to a crazy oldtimer who works in the hold.

A Walking Boss (off stage): Let's go-o-o!!

Interior: the Shed

as the men head down the wide aisle, past pallets of coffee and a variety of other goods. A cold wind whips through the shed.

The CAMERA TAKES Bart and Julie HEAD-ON. Julie looks exhausted and downcast — and Bart notices it.

Bart: You in a hell of a shape to woik coffee. You drunk last night?

Julie: Ahh . . . a little . . . Lydia and I got into a beef. She took a hike on me in the middle of the night.

Bart: I al'us said she was a lady with a lotta class.

Bart glances at him, then does a double-take.

Bart: You bullshittin' me, broth'a?

Julie shakes his head.

Bart: Ouch! What happened, my man?

Julie: It all started because I told her I was goin' back in the hold. But there's got to be more to it than that.

Bart: That for *damn* sure.

Exterior: the Ship

The men tramp heavily up the gangway, then spread fore and aft to their assigned hatches.

Montana and his gang stand at the hatch coaming and look below.

Montana: The work's down below, gentlemen. Get down there and shake hands with the cargo.

Julie looks at the vertical ladder leading below — and feels butterflies in his stomach: It's been a long time. He swings one leg over the coaming and starts down.

Interior: the Hold

Six men (the usual racial mixture) stand in the square of the hatch looking at the tons of coffee bags. Four of them pair off naturally, leaving Julie and a young BLACK MAN as the third set of partners. He's a handsome slender man in his late twenties, with a goatee and a "natural" hair style, with a black beret pulled rakishly down over one ear.

Julie: Well—guess it's you an' me.

Black Guy (sullenly): Whatever . . .

Shannon puts his hand out.

Julie: My name's Shannon.

The Black Man stares at his outstretched hand for a moment, then slowly removes one glove and gives Shannon a limp, self-conscious handshake but doesn't look at him.

Black Man: Evans.

Off stage we HEAR the NOISE of the ELECTRIC WINCHES start up. The men move out of the square of the hatch as if on command.

A stack of pallet boards descends into the hold, held together by a bar bridle. CAMERA HOLDS on the load until it is landed in the square by two of the men.

Random shots of the work getting underway, switching from two longshoremen on one side to the two on the other, the CAMERA NOTING that the other two men are sitting down, that only four men work at the same time. (NOTE: When loading cargo, there will be eight men in the hold.) Heavy iron rollers are set up so that the boards can be pushed back into the wings to get to the coffee.

Evans pulls a small sack hook from his back pocket and gets ready. Julie pulls out his big hook and Evans' eyes widen.

Evans: What'cha doin' with that antique? You can't work coffee with that thing.

Julie (smiles): Uh—it's the only one I brought. It'll have to do.

They dig their hooks into one corner of a bag, their hands into the other and lift, tossing the 170-pound sack onto a back corner of the board.

Another sack to the other corner, a loud grunt from Julie, and they keep at it, awkwardly, neither man adjusted yet to the other man's rhythm.

Julie: To me . . . now to you . . . no, no, my side, my side.

Three sacks high, four stacks, but they can't get together, Evans leaning one way, Shannon the other. In minutes they're breathing hard and Shannon begins to sweat.

Julie (panting): Let me show you, pardner. Work easy, work easy . . .

Evans: We're doin' this like old people fuck, man . . .

Julie (laughing): Worse'n that . . . c'mon, let's go, the hook's hangin'.

The bar bridle sways back and forth 10 feet above the deck — on their side of the ship, indicating it is their load.

On the other side of the hatch, the other two longshoremen lean casually on their finished load, smiling across at Shannon and Evans — and their predicament.

Finally Julie and Evans get a load finished; they push the board out into the square of the hatch and hook it up and the winch driver takes it out. Then they move back and start another load.

Various angles as the struggle continues: They bump heads, they stagger, curse each other under their breaths, glare at each other angrily.

Evans: Man, when's the last time you worked coffee?

Shannon: I was workin' coffee before you made it down to the street corner. My side—now yours, that's it, you're gettin' the hang of it.

That's too much for Evans. He stops, backs off, walks around, looks across at the other two men.

Evans (angrily): Ain't this some shit?! This oldtimer comin' down into the hold and tellin' me like it is. I'll be a *mother*fucker! Man, I'm gonna call the hall and get me a replacement.

First Longshoreman (to Evans): Your load, babe.

Voice from on Deck: Hey, down below! What the hell's goin' on? Let's get the cargo out!

The Walking Boss glares down over the coaming.

Shannon charges out of the wing like a boxer coming out of his corner. He stands in the center of the ship's hatch and squints up at the Walking Boss, hands on his hips.

Julie: Don't sweat it—we'll get the *fuckin'* cargo out! We're clear back in the wing and we're using shitty equipment that should'a been thrown over the side twenty years ago! Just hang onto your ass, Tompkins.

He moves back into the wing and rejoins Evans, who is looking him over for the first time.

Julie: Asshole. I knew that guy when he didn't know how to rig fuckin' gear.

In a corner of the hatch, sitting on some coffee sacks, the two Longshoremen who are on break watch Julie work.

Third Longshoreman: Who's that dude, anyway? I never seen him in the hold before.

Fourth Longshoreman: That's Shannon. He's no longshoreman—he's a stevedore. There's a difference. Used to be big in the union. An old southpaw, too.

Third Longshoreman: He must'a slipped his motherfuckin' trolley, takin' a coffee job his age.

Across from them Julie suddenly stops working and looks at Evans. He wipes the sweat from his face.

Julie: What's your first name, Evans?

Evans (beat): Eve.

Julie: Eve?! You're kiddin'. You mean like in Adam and—

Evans (rudely): —No, man! Those are my *initials. Everett—Vachel—Evans. E* period *V* period *E* period! You dig? They call me Eve for short.

Julie: Oh, yeah. Sure. I dig.

Evans: But I don't give a fuck what you call me, man. It's an eight-hour day far's I'm concerned. Then I don't have to look at your ugly face again. C'mon, let's pump this coffee out'a here. I'm tired of messin' with it.

Shannon grins and plunges to work.

Julie: Right on, brother.   *Cut to:*

Exterior: Pier 19—Day

A horde of longshoremen streaming out of the pier at five o'clock, among them an exhausted Julie Shannon and E.V.E. Evans. Heavy traffic flows along the Embarcadero. As Evans starts off in another direction, Shannon gestures for him to hold up.

Julie: Uh—I been thinkin'. You want to try it again tomorrow?

Evans (suspiciously): You mean work partners?

Julie: Yeah. I'll pick us up a job. You can stay in the sack 'til I call you.

Evans studies him for a long beat, as if he suspects something.

Julie (grins): What do you think?

Evans shrugs nonchalantly, sways back and forth, looking everywhere but at Shannon.

Evans: Suit yourself, man. I can dig stayin' in bed. But don't be doin' me no favors, you know?

Julie: Don't worry about it.

He takes a pen and his time book out of his shirt pocket.

Julie: What's your brass number?

Evans: Seventy-seven forty-seven.

Julie: And your phone?

Exterior: an Apartment—Evening

A lovely old Victorian, two-story flat on the side of Telegraph Hill in San Francisco.

Interior: the Apartment

A comfortably furnished, burrowed-in feeling, with floor-to-ceiling bookcases, a fireplace, deep couches . . .

Lydia Shannon is curled up on a cushioned bench seat in front of a large picture window. She looks lonely, yet introspective, and her gaze is on the bay and waterfront below.

Robin Smith breezes into the living room from her bedroom, dressed for the evening. She opens a coat closet.

Robin: Lyd, you're sure you won't come along?

Lydia: No, really, I'll be fine.

Robin: OK, love. I won't be late. If you're up we'll have a nightcap, maybe chat for a bit. See you later.

Lydia: Have fun.

Robin leaves — and Lydia gets up to go to the kitchen, passing on the way a window that looks out on the street. She glances out, then freezes.

Julie is getting out of his car across the street. He starts toward the apartment.

Lydia doesn't know what to do; she starts toward the kitchen, then turns and sits down on a couch; she gets up, paces, her eyes excited and hopeful, yet confused, uncertain.

Exterior: the Apartment

Julie enters and starts up the steps. He looks uncertain, too.

Interior: the Apartment

Now Lydia can hear his STEPS on the stairs, coming closer . . . until he reaches the hallway, the FLOOR CREAKING under his FOOTSTEPS.

Exterior: the Hallway

Julie gets to the door, starts to knock but can't; pride, stubbornness — whatever it is, he can't do it; so he turns and starts back down the hall.

Interior: the Apartment

Lydia hears the FADING FOOTSTEPS and runs to the door as if to open it and go after him; but she can't either, and for the same reasons. His FOOTSTEPS FADE OUT.

Saddened, she walks over to the window and watches him cross the street, walking stiffly from a hard day's work. Tears fill her eyes.

Interrelationships and Introspection

Caffeine Dreams

Bad night
at the end
of a boredom busy day.
Staring across a gaunt
intersection
of barren thoughts,
cursing quarts of coffee
so carelessly consumed
to fill daytime deadspace.

Inspiration:
Walk
along the bay
and watch the night wind
score the sand
into scarred symphonies;
Listen to seagrass
weep
in the running tide.

I step over
driftwood dung
dropped by some
apocalyptic rider.
Two starfish
cling swollen
to a damp asphalt rock:
junkyard jewels
waiting
for a dry sky
in which to die
and glitter for eternity—
rusted splotches
on a seaside lamp post.

I seduce the sun
over the shoreside hills
with an emotional striptease,
Toying with strands of
guilt and recrimination,
Revealing dreams of saintly
salvage.

Pastel moonface
snickers gently
at my scattered costume
and turns me home,
stopping only
for Perrier and Postum,
Content to let
the stars in my sky
sleep at last.

The Answered Question

What Kind of Song do you Sing
to the Child of your mind?—
I should say "I"—for it is I
who is seeking the words and the Tune.

Fantasize—What child do you See?
Is it calm?
Is it Peaceful
Where this child sits—or is it
Violent and Unfulfilled?

I don't know why I ask You—
When it is I who is seeking
His whereabouts.

Is the child only a dream—or is
the Child someone that you really see?
Does the child stand free or is He Bound
By strong ropes of Mind and Matter?

It is my child—I don't know Why
I ask you—unless
You See objectively—
That which I cannot
or that—Which in Truth is a
Figment of my Mind.

In My Blindness I look upon you to
Reflect My Image Both Real and of Fantasy—
When it is I who should be
Seeing "I" Through Me—
It is My Song—
It is My Vision—
It is My Place
To Find Me!

My House

I live alone
In a dwelling of my mind.
Distant from reality—
Yet so close that my machinations
seem to me—real.

The house I live in
has walls and no walls.
Windowed spaces fit within
Windowless Frames and
Doors exist only as
Thresholds—the open
one negated by the closed.

I sit, looking out, and see
The reflection of me looking in
and wonder which is really me.
I am alone no matter which
Way it may be.

I walk through the endless
Forests within my house.
Some days with dread fear.
I never seem to stop—Asleep
or Awake, it makes no difference.
My reality is as much a dream
as it is a reality.

Sometimes I hear my own breath
and feel it is anothers. Then
there are times when the sound
of my footsteps will make me shudder.
For in my loneliness I am aware
That others do exist.

I live alone
Locked in by my thoughts.
Some days my house is full
And I feel real—those days
Are all too few. Most days
my house is barren. The only
comforts then are those that
I will allow. For you see—
I live alone—within Me!

My choice is made through Fear.
Outwardly, it would appear
That this should not be so.
But since I never see what others
see of me, I fear that what they
See is ugly. In this light my choice
is real. Fear alone has built my house
and I am the only one with a key.

VAWTER

No Epitaph

Between the bleached stones
of a lizards' playground,
in a canyon near Chico,
a river runs again
taunting tomorrow's drought.
I wonder: Has it
retraced its steps of '71
or erased mine and hers too?

We met at a country dancehall
when the night was upside down:
Snowdrifts filled the sky,
the moon lay glistening on the ground.

I still don't know what touched
when I moved inside her shadow,
but I was welcomed with a smile.

She smelled of dreams,
her voice the promise of satin sheets.
On her upper lip
the hint of a scar
carved by a kamikaze butterfly.

Our bellies burst into stardust
as they rubbed
beneath disco sheets of sound.

I gave her my heart
gift-wrapped in lavender.
She gave me a volcano
of rose petals.

At first the only sound
was the burp of the candle flame
bothered by the breeze
of bodies bumping.

Then the bed
shook and shattered
with the suddenness
of a cowboy's temper tantrum.

A patch of sleep covered
the dead eye of the storm.

Our chromosomes
chattered through the night,
discussing details so intimate
there was a rush
of embarrassed recognition
when our eyes met at dawn
before the morning kiss.

I was devastated years later
when she called
across a continent,
dilated with dope,
to hazily inquire:
Did we ever sleep together?

Some days I awake
determined to kill her memory,
but it lives,
indelible as the colors
of a tropical honeymoon
painted by a widower
in the half-lit room
of his retirement hotel.

Depression

I wait Day by Day
For Light of some kind.
I wait in a deep gray mist—
For Something—I'm not sure What!

I wait—the characters pass—
faceless—voices float by—
devoid of recognizable patterns.
The Mist writhes about my body and
I am encased in a slowly whirling
vortex of Nothingness.

I wait in elasticized time—
Hours—snap in and out of minutes—
Days ferment and the odor of wasted
Time Sickens Me.

I Wait—the Mist is fetid and Humid.
The Sweat of a prickled anxiety
falls in little rills all over Me.

I wait—in Awe of my mind—
breached in an Agony of
Thoughts encrusted in
Scabby Inertia.

I Wait—For Something—
I wait—Silence Shatters
the Veil into Myriad
Splinters of Thought.

I reach up—blinded by
The mirror of my Mind—
Groping and Grasping in
Desperation—Trying to cling
To One Idea!

I Stand Paralyzed—
As the Last Thought
Passes By.

Ridiculous Secrets

I'd flown to Luxembourg just as planned, that quiet city in a little country that doesn't ever want to change. It insists on remaining bucolic, peaceful, and primitive without regard to modern invention and so-called progress. This is an outlook I can well understand, although stasis of any sort has a decaying effect on human nature. Could we imagine ourselves to be a race of people with the infinite capacity for technological knowledge who yet refuse to put it into practice, who prefer to till a ruddy soil with their own hands, to look up into the sky on a starry night and say to themselves, "There's a universe out there. We can go to its end if we want to, but we are content to remain right here. We can even make ourselves immortal, but we prefer to stay on earth until our bones kick up the sod and we pass into the realm of darkness or true light." I declare such a state is possible but would it be satisfying? I cannot see it. I'm sure most people can't. I want to reach the stars.

Such thoughts went through my head. That was before I decided to take this trip and, at exactly the right moment with the right setting, end it all. Let the human race do what it wanted to. I, for one, would have no part in the fiasco I called *mankind*. Even as a child, I had been curious, and now I knew I'd considered every logical possibility for my survival, but there was no other way out.

One ironic circumstance of my flight was the tiny Derringer I'd smuggled from New York in my suitcase, merely a 22, but enough to do the job. I can't say why they didn't detect it with their scientific inventions, but perhaps it was because the baggage goes in a place that is inaccessible to the passengers and they didn't care, or maybe it was human error—the suitcase checker had a hangover. Actually, I was wishing they would have found it, then my chances of sudden death would have been almost wholly diminished. I certainly wasn't going to take an overdose of sleeping pills; one bullet in the right spot of the temple would be just perfect. It would be over in a flash. There'd be powder burns on my face, a hole in my head, and Don Tracey would be found lying on the floor of his room whose windows viewed the Basilica and Herr Bauer's garden.

I certainly could never buy a gun in Germany, although I

might have my friend professor Hans Kerlacher purchase one for me. Hans is suspicious. He has the German mind. He'd want a dossier on what I was going to use the gun for. Moreover, Hans, like most Germans, is a good psychologist. He'd see right through me. No one must suspect a thing. I must keep my secret even from Hans. When they find me, of course, not even secrets will matter then.

Yes, I'll admit, I shall be excited to get it over with. My own death gives me something to look forward to for my body and mind shall seek this experience, one of the most obscure phenomena known to man. No one has ever come back to tell the tale, and it looks as though no one ever will, unless one gives credence to worn-out myths. There's something very ingenious in death. Perhaps it's as simple as the image in the mirror, which is always reversed yet mystifies the most renowned of physicists.

I am quite safe now, however, for, also as planned, I am on the train with my suitcase, on my way to Koln, that dank Gothic city where gorgons and demons lurk on every facade. We like it, admit it to romanticize the dark side of our natures. Not too long ago this was exemplified on a worldwide basis. This demon was in the form of a man. I know the very perch on the building from which he was stolen. Undoubtedly, he changed into human form, and for five years came to remind man of his own demon. He did quite well, and for me such dark things are not so easily effaced. I intend to carry my secrets with me.

But as I say, I am looking forward not only to my death, but also to my reunion with Hans. It has been five years since I've seen him. We met over a beer and schnitzels a long time ago after the war in that manufacturing town of Hanover. I was then a reporter in the army. He spoke excellent English, and since then I have met him squarely by learning German. Now we speak incongruously, but we discuss the most profound ideas in literature, art, and philosophy. It is certainly worthwhile to come halfway across the world to find someone to talk to in this non-forensic age.

Hans has been able to engage the very same rooms I had the last time I visited Munchen. I have planned everything thoroughly. For instance, I realize that it is sort of a dirty trick to play on my friend by shooting myself in the rooms that he provided for me.

It behooves me to know the hotel I shall stay in tonight even if I have to pay for a double. Tomorrow I shall stand in front of the

Dom, which is one of the world's tallest churches—there's another taller in France or somewhere, I believe . . . then go inside to stare up at the prodigious vaulted ceiling. What on earth did man have in mind to construct such a building? It has no utility except an esthetic one. It is not a hotel that lodges people. Men died in its conception. That is a fact. Each workman took pride in each block of granite he set. This idea pleases me; a concept our modern day workman has quite lost. Yes, tomorrow I shall look at this church, take a train to Koblentz and ride the ferry down the Rhine past the old castles that used to guard the river; then on to Munchen. Perhaps I shall even have a glass of wine or so, a whole bottle, get drunk and forget the entire thing; visit Hans, go to concerts, beer halls, etc. . . . This I knew I would not do. My past attests to it.

A very little on that subject will be in order. I am a successful reporter in my own right for a paper that has integrity, there being approximately three or four in the entire country, and my column is syndicated. Let me tell you that this is a distinction that only a handful of reporters out of millions ever attain. How did I manage it? Hard work, competition. I became the rugged American individualist, cutting the throats of his fellow man, but always with a smile. I never had any qualms in practicing social Darwinism, besides it's natural in us. When a hot story would come up, I'd get there first. My writing improved as did my world perspective, so that I finally reached the spot where I was considered a competent analyst on world affairs. New York thinks I am merely on a vacation and that in three weeks I'll be back at my office in front of the typewriter, pecking out a competent analysis of the current German social system. How little those imbeciles know. The German social system is the farthest thing from my mind; any social system is, for that matter. Man is socializing himself into self-destruction.

Yes, I might say I have seen a good deal at the age of fifty-eight. I've been married, have grown children, and am not proud to say I'm a grandfather. My kids are raised, the wife has remarried. I have no filial responsibilities. There was a pretty little number about thirty years my junior whom I'd been seeing, but I was jilted by, of all things, a full-blooded American who practices Hinduism and thinks he's some sort of ascetic. He collects welfare—which my salary pays for—and claims he transcends being, a concept difficult enough to formulate, let alone attain. Of course he is thirty years younger than I am also, but he doesn't have half the drive and stamina. Well, then, let them have one another. Charlotte said to me at our final parting, "You're just too nervous for me to be around, Charles. You never relax. You're always on the go. What do you think you're accomplishing, anyway? Tom is so—"

"Listen," I said. "Don't tell me about that hare-brained ascetic of yours who sits on his butt all day harmonizing with nature while I feed him. I've got a job to do, and it's not easy. I've got deadlines to meet."

We had a pitched battle over that and parted. Charlotte worked. I could not understand what she saw in this sloth. I'd even met him, and he wasn't interesting. All he did was to nod and say "Umm" to any questions. Personally I think she had been bewitched, and I was expecting her to come to her senses until I heard they were getting married. This struck me hard, for I'd been quite a bit in love with her but I do not maintain it is one of the reasons for my recent decision. I know man commits suicide over rather obvious and material things: loss of fortune, love, health, etc. None of these had anything to do with my basic reason, which was strictly metaphysical. Unknown to myself, during the course of my job, I'd been unconsciously accumulating data, which all of a sudden overwhelmed me one day while I was at work. All I can say is it had something to do with man's most inner nature that was somehow tainted, and the facts rendered this evaluation positively frightening. It was right then that I decided to turn in my cards. And it is right now that I am about to do so.

I did just as I said I would. I went down the Rhine, I got drunk, had some vicious nightmares back in my hotel room, and said goodbye to the Dom in the morning. It would, after all, be the last time I'd see this magnificent structure. Then I wrote a post-card to my daughter Suzanne, my only real tie left with this world. In it I did not indicate my unbalanced state of mind. After all this was over, she'd be able to say with quite a clear conscience to her husband (a good surgeon), "Daddy seemed so peaceful in his letter. He was enjoying his trip. No one would have ever thought. . . ." Then she'd break down into tears, and that would be the last time she'd think of me. My act would gradually wear her spirit down to acknowledge that her father had had to take that way out. They could think anything they wanted—that I was selfish, cowardly, etc. This certainly had no effect on me. If they knew what I did about man, they'd commit suicide too, as would the entire species.

I left the hotel in Koln, and took the train to Munchen. The German countryside in summer is beautiful, even from a second-class compartment. I never traveled first class on any of my world-wide trips. The forests are thick, and the trees straight as poles—so close together that one can't help admiring the vivacity of the soil. The smell of the pines is intoxicating, and all through the forests lurk Bavarian farmhouses, which harbor hard-working people. They plant potatoes, radishes, wheat, barley, and rye, and the horses and cows are as fat and healthy as the people. Gradually, as one approaches the city of Munchen, factories pop up here and there until one realizes one is in the center of an industrial city, from whose large stacks dark smoke emanates. One is reminded of the Ruhr, which supplied the war effort against the entire world. There is a lot of chatter on the train; people leap up and stand at the windows for the arrival, and so on. I did, also, realizing as I did so that I had one, maybe two days left in the world.

When we came to a stop, I was fighting and pushing in line to get off just like the others. I had one little suitcase and a shoulder bag. I always carried my own things, for although I am not young any more, I walk a good deal to keep in shape. When a porter came up to me, I said, in quite fluent German, that I didn't need any assistance. He looked oddly at me, for he'd been certain I was a foreigner and now he was uncertain.

One would not think that an ordinary train station could be a source of joy, but it had been five years since I'd been in Bavaria, and the setting was as important to me as the renewal of acquaintances. As was usual for summertime, there were hundreds of Americans wandering about with their knapsacks. For the most part they were innocent kids, traveling abroad for the first time. I had brought my children over when they were that age. If nothing else, it was an experience that rounded out one's education. After all, the classic tradition certainly did not originate in America, although it might well have ended there. Young minds are curious, and form structures curiosity, I find, more than it deteriorates it.

The large clock on the lamppost outside, startled me for a moment. It was two-thirty. I'd forgotten to set back my watch, although I'd been in Germany for two days. I quickly set it, crossed the street, and walked down a little side street to 19 Ringstrasse. The Germans maintained the frenetic driving conditions that prevailed in Europe. They tried to run you down if they could, and their horns worked constantly. Even on this side street, I almost got run down, and I shouted German imprecations after the S.O.B. I did stop in a little candy store and bought some of my favorite rock candy, which I cannot get in the United States, for everything is made through Langendorf. I recognized the same middle-aged woman who was here five years ago. So many people come and go. She did not remember me. Other customers made a reminiscence impossible, and when I again walked down the street, I stuffed the candy into my pocket and forgot about it. I was still cursing that crazy driver. He might have killed me. It was one thing to take one's own life, another to have some other S.O.B. do it.

I purposely put off visiting my favorite antique store (my daughter wanted me to buy and send her a mantel clock), since I wanted to reach my rooms and was tired after my journey. After all, was it worth it taking one's life at this stage of the game? I was convinced that it was, now more so than ever.

The side street opened onto a circular plaza, the Ringstrasse. A fountain stood in the middle, and my house was just across the street, a granite structure with bronze balconies and griffons on the facade. My adrenalin surged, but this was mixed with an indefinable longing or sadness, a quality of emotion that I'd never really felt before. I was like Moses sitting in judgment of man, a very disquieting task. I did not stop at the fountain, but rang my doorbell. It was answered by Frau Becker. She looked even older than she had the last time. She and her husband owned the lodging. "Ah, Frau Becker," I said. "It's me, Don Tracey, the American. Herr Professor has arranged for me to take rooms." She didn't recognize me. Her hair was white, and her ankles were swollen from the gout. Her cheeks were rosy, and she'd wrinkled extraordinarily. "Oh," she said finally forcing a smile. "Herr Professor, the American!" She had recognized me, but without any more formality she showed me to my rooms—which I might easily have found myself, but it is polite to follow customs. She could hardly make the stairs. I smiled inwardly. Christ, I would be better off committing suicide for that reason alone, that I shouldn't become decrepit like her. I didn't even need any metaphysical considerations.

She let me into my rooms, made certain I had towels and soap, and departed, leaving me in peace. The trip had been harrowing. The two large rooms were in the back of the building, with high ceilings and wooden paneling. They were furnished with old things, which by now could be called antique. There was even an old floor clock that worked and chimed. One of the strange reasons I'd wanted to get these rooms was to hear the clock chime again. Then I could rest in peace. Actually, I'd been fortunate to get these rooms, for this was not a hotel. They served breakfast, continental style, but in his letter Hans had told me the Beckers did not keep as many lodgers as they used to, so the rooms had been vacant.

I deposited my things on a dressing table, appreciated the hand-carved bed and my inlaid writing desk, and, in the main room, stood in front of the fireplace and admired the oriental rug. Why, when I'd been a mere youth in my thirties, these things had been a great inspiration to me! I guess there was some of that nostalgia now. I went to the window and threw open the shutters. The view disclosed a small but beautiful garden. It was still there! I was not familiar with horticulture or the generic names of flowers, but there were green hedges, statues, a goldfish pond, and rows of the

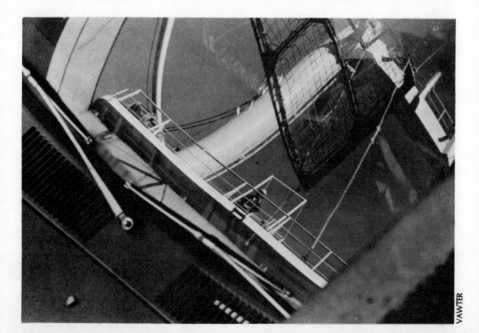

VAWTER

starkest flowers, along with numerous trees. This garden belongs to the house next door, Herr Bauer's, whose acquaintance I'd also made, and his rake was stuck upright in the ground. He must still be alive, this old man, for that was the symbol by which I knew him, short of actually encountering him. He always stuck the rake into the earth, upside down, after working. His sons never did that. I'd watched them all work in the garden for hours. So then. . . .

I was tired, I admitted to myself. I took out a bottle of Scotch I'd brought with me, poured myself a shot, downed it, and passed out on the embroidered quilt on top of my bed.

Some time in the afternoon, the phone rang. I answered it sleepily. It was the professor. I was expected for dinner at seven o'clock. It was already half past five. I arose, poured myself another drink, and began to run the water into the tub, which was one of those large ones that is almost the size of a swimming pool, but in which one can comfortably suspend one's body, turning off the harshness of gravity. Then I dressed in one of my lighter flannel suits, doffed my hat, and walked the five blocks to the Kerlacher's. Their house was not unlike many others from the outside, but their rooms were some of the most beautiful I'd ever seen in my life. All the floors were parquet, hardwood, covered with oriental rugs. On their walls hung tapestries and paintings, and their furniture was old but refined. It was easy to see how their artists could live symbols. I knocked with the bronze ring, which was ensconced in a lion's head.

Frau Kerlacher answered and escorted me into the living room where I was to encounter the professor. We shook hands heartily, but our renewal of acquaintance had an inward hue to it, which I find is true of reunions with most Germans. I sat down in the living room, and Frau Kerlacher brought me a large stein of German beer. I preferred Scotch, but realized that throughout dinner and for the rest of the evening we'd be drinking beer. This is what the professor and most Germans drank—a custom. We sat there and reminisced about old times, right after the war and later.

"Ah, but,—" I said, in my rusty German. "I don't know how you do it. The silos are full of wheat, the cows fat, and the iron mills are incredible. In the fields, everywhere, I see new machinery." The professor took my comment laconically with nonchalance. "The war was nothing for us," he said. "That we could not rebuild the next day." And although the professor was a large boisterous sort, I took his comment to mean that those who did not belong to the Nazi Party had their strength before Hitler's advent and had maintained it. I found this quite a stimulating attitude on the part of many Germans. Of course, some had followed the party, but even in these I saw a begrudging sense of having erred. After all, it was not so long ago that Germany was officially an occupied territory. Of course, the youth had experienced none of this. They wanted new cars, television sets, sports equipment and so on, just like the Americans. They had merely supplanted one false value with another, but the second was less harmless—or was it?

"The youth here are just as hopeless," I said abruptly.

"What? Explain?" The professor smiled.

"All they want are new toys. They've forgotten the intellectual values that we've inherited from the Greeks."

"Yes," he said. "They do not believe in Homer or Pindar. They want something new. We're on the verge of a new culture."

I thought this a stimulating idea, and we pursued it, until we arrived at the synthesis of all cultures. So far neither his wife nor the professor had an inkling that there was something wrong with me. We ended the discussion and went into dinner where the Frau had set the table with sauerbraten and potato pancakes. She was an excellent cook, and I loved German food. I found it highly ironic, since I was not of German but of Italian-French ancestry, that I loved the German culture above any. Frau Kerlacher was a pretty woman whose hair was still blond. She wore an apron and was hefty, a typical German woman. She was energetic and demonstrative, but definitely not my type. I liked the more frail femininity of the French.

We had a marvelous dinner, during the course of which the Professor asked me if I'd read the book of Hermann Broch's that he sent me in the original.

"Of course," I said. "It's highly pantheistic, but I think it's the finest single work of literature to come out of the modern age. I feel much closer to him than to Joyce."

"Ja, ja, Joyce is too desultory," he answered. "One can't follow him, and if one can, so what?" I found some merit in this statement, but not because the professor taught German literature. I'd always been fond of German writers.

After a dessert of fresh fruit cocktail and pastries, the professor and I went out for a walk. Of course, I knew immediately where we were going, to his favorite drinking place, the Hofbrauhouse, an old German beer hall. I kept mute, for our mere walking along, and my knowing where we were going (which place I wanted to attend anyway), and knowing also that the professor felt it to be a surprise all brought a great joy to me, which joy I was certain was the germ of our very gaiety in living. If only I could make such a state more constant—but it was too late for me. I'd seen right down to the very core of being.

The professor took a circuitous route, past several old churches and through several alleyways I'd never before explored, but presently, on the corner, we came to the beer hall with its revelers and spritely Bavarian music. We emerged from the dark streets into the well-lit rooms, which are almost always crowded. I had to stop for a moment to look up at the strange peasant faces that are painted on the ceilings. They were so beautiful, I could almost cry. At what step along the way had I lost that peasant zest for life no matter how bad the conditions?

We sat in a corner, and immediately two large mugs of beer were set in front of us. The band, in short pants and Tyrolian vests, played endlessly. The young Americans hollered innocently, but without empathy, and everyone sang and reveled, including the professor and I. Remember, I thought my play acting must be thorough. We sat there until past midnight, and as the beer took its progressive effect, I became more glib. "My daughter's getting bored with her marriage," I told the professor. "She wants to write a novel, can you believe that?"

"Ah, ha, let her do so. You should encourage her. The ability is inborn. I follow your articles every week in the *Times,* very good, perceptive. I am surprised you were not born a German." Naturally I was proud of the compliment, but I did not allude to it. I relaxed and said, "Well, it's better for her to be engrossed in something, even if it's a novel, if it'll save her marriage. She also wants an antique mantel clock. I was wondering if you . . . ?"

"Ah," he said. "This takes a little time. On Saturday, we have to drive to a little town near Ulm. I know of a dealer there where you can get the real thing." I, of course, would not be here Saturday, but I couldn't tell him that. I merely nodded appreciatively. It felt good to know someone who knew where one could come across a real clock like that. I had just such a shop in my mind's eye. We must have clinked glasses and drunk about ten liters of beer apiece, before we got out of there. I couldn't count the number of times I had gone to the bathroom. When we finally did leave, we staggered home, singing German songs, which was merely a facade for me. Even the professor's taking me tomorrow night to an organ concert in one of the old churches, where we'd listen to Pachelbel, Buxtahude, Bach, and Praetorius, was a myth. Tomorrow, my schedule was set. Tomorrow was my day. We left each other the best of old friends, and I staggered home among the dark fauns and satyrs that sat on the cornices of the houses to get my last night's sleep.

In the morning, a very hot bath dispelled my hangover. Then I dressed in casual clothes, slacks, a short-sleeved shirt, loafers—nothing like what our young generation calls casual, almost bare-skinned—and went down to breakfast. The Beckers always served a hearty breakfast, eggs, ham, toast, and jams with tea or coffee and juice, and I ate the entire thing, but I got satisfaction from none of it. I couldn't sense that the food even went down. Again, in my rooms, I peeked out into the garden and saw Herr Bauer, an older man in his straw hat and overalls, stooping over his hoe. I was certain he was still around, but I wasn't about to disturb him now.

With my toilet attended to, I left the house, and walked briskly to the Alte Pinotek, the gallery that I liked best of all in Munich if not in the entire world. I arrived at the museum just as they were opening, paid and went in. My last aesthetic appreciation was to be of the paintings of Hans Holbein, and Brueghel the Elder, and of the old German masters. Too bad it was not to be of the Pantheon. I did not feel maudlin over this. I felt my choice was quite worthy of my last one. I perused the paintings briefly, but sumptuously absorbed them. I can't describe their beauty. Perhaps it had something to do with my state, perhaps not. The forests, the rivers, the lakes and mountains almost could have been from other planets, and those faces were exactly like those of androids. Underneath it all was a race of superior intelligence who would take over the universe when man was effaced from this planet, and I was certain that would be soon.

When my morning's viewing was over, I returned to my rooms, loaded the single-shot Derringer, and laid the gun on the marble table next to me. Actually, this morning, I'd been dressing for this occasion, no other. I was to give myself one brief review of my reasons for this act, and the act would soon be my last one ever.

Since, and perhaps even before I'd been working on the newspapers, I'd been privy to certain details and facts of information that are not readily accessible to the ordinary man. The religions of the world, for instance, were each and every one of them a lie. There was no God whatsoever. Life on this planet—and elsewhere—had been an accident, nothing more; it has now been reproduced synthetically and soon will be so down to the very creature we call *man*. The Vatican's holdings were enormous. It owned half the world and was responsible for at least half the wars on the globe. Not to single out Catholicism. The Hindus, Sikhs, Buddhists, and Protestants were involved over strife of some sort or another, whether it be martial or civil—and hadn't large countries fought and hundreds of thousands been massacred over whether the Trinity was three in one, or one in three? This is just to get started on the great religions of the world.

Let us take our great nations. They ostentatiously proclaim they are desirous of peace, but underneath it all—I shall spare you the statistics—they are involved in the most panicked arms race believable. And the weapons they are inventing via modern science are too hideous to describe. What's more, they are under the delusion that these devices are merely demonstrative. They will never be used, not until the first spark is struck. Man does not make weapons not to use them. He never has; that is not his nature.

Then what is the goal of each of these nations except to accumulate riches, which are kept in the hands of the few, and to bring its neighboring country to its knees. And, of course, all this while they are straining beyond credulity the world's resources, which simply cannot be replaced, for they have been broken down into other molecular ingredients. We cannot breathe unpolluted air any more, and our fish have been all but extinguished from the seas. We are cutting off our life supports. We don't like life—admit it. It is the race who is committing suicide, not me by my singular, meaningless act.

Mere gangsters run the most profitable countries, a long cry from our Hadrians and our Aurelius, and all each individual can think of is to amass his own private fortune to the detriment of his fellow man, so that he does not have to work but can pass his remaining days leisurely. I can tell you that one individual life means nothing. The slightest alteration in our universe crushes it like a human would crush a fly. And the same protocol man deals to his fellow man, one nation deals to another.

The church as well as man's pride keeps the population explosion going, only the very richest are entitled to adequate medical treatment, and the very attitude of so-called big business is to turn its head away from any disastrous truth that does not drastically affect us today. For them, tomorrow does not count, but here is the catch. Tomorrow is here. Tomorrow is today, for even if we about-faced, we are already too late. I'll admit these facts are accessible to one who cares, and I am one of those. That is the very reason I can't stand to sit by and watch all this go on. It is intolerable to me, and there is nothing I can do about it. I have tried to slant my articles to point to the truth, but they were censored. I had even thought of starting my own paper, but I could not get circulation.

The entire object of my bringing these things up was to see if there was one ray of hope, a chink in my argument that would lead me to change my mind. I find none, as I am sure the reader does not. I certainly felt like the man who plays Russian roulette, but I had no chance, so to speak. In this little gun, there was only one chamber. I was sweating profusely. The final moment is not funny. A sunbeam from the window had touched my table. I raised the gun up to my temple. I'd memorized the very spot.

As to what happened at that moment, I can scarcely assess. I know a bird landed on the window sill; probably a robin, but most certainly the largest I'd ever seen in my life—more like an eagle. I did not pull the trigger, and the church bells seemed to gong simultaneously with all this. It seemed for a moment that I was in another world. The room became enormous, surreal. My entire body had been drenched in sweat in just those few minutes. If I lived through this, I'd have to change clothes. But, sure enough, there was the reason before me, simple, yet wholly complex, the one thing that had avoided all my analysis and my saving principle. An inner voice said (I quote), "What's the use in taking your own life? Certainly man is going to perpetrate genocide, and very soon, and you have a very general idea of how he's going to go about it. But just think—you do not know the particulars, whether it be mass starvation, a partial atomic war with accompanying radiation, sickness, etc. Just think, if you live you can observe the direction of these particulars. This is your raison d'etre."

You can't imagine how overjoyed I was at this revelation. I put down the gun immediately and banished it from my thoughts, forever. Now I had hope. Why hadn't I seen such a simple solution?

Think how interesting it would be to prove the unknown details of man's destruction. Why should I take my own life, when I could have it done for me? I can assure you this is the only consideration that kept me alive, and quite a morbid one at that.

While I bathed again, the will to live returned. I did not feel I had backed out. I had found the solution I'd been searching for, the only possible one. I made all sorts of plans, the first of which was to effect my retirement as soon as I returned, the second of which was to visit Rome. But subservient to none of these was the will to change from a person who went after everything tenaciously to a person who merely sat back and observed, watched things go by. And I can assure you this had nothing to do with those laissez faire religions that are nowadays so popular with young people.

Gradually, temporal reality returned. I would drive to Ulm on Saturday and buy my daughter that clock, and attend that concert tonight with the professor after all. I cannot say I was exuberant over my discovery—but satisfied, yes.

Over dinner that night, the professor even noticed my jovial mood. "What makes you so giddy, Thomas?" he said. I toasted the champagne. "Did you ever read," I said, "or remember reading a story by Dostoevsky. I believe it was called, 'The Dream of a Ridiculous Man,' and that it went something like this. A man sat by a table that had a pistol on it. He was about to commit suicide, but in his last-minute thoughts, via some extraordinary rationalizations and a lot of faith, he convinced himself not to commit his final act."

"I don't remember the story," said the professor, and then Frau Kerlacher said, "But do go on. What was his decision? What did it entail?"

"Oh," I answered nonchalantly. "I don't remember the details exactly either. It was just that he decided all the things he thought that were so bad, and driving him to this act, weren't really so bad after all."

"Then he was at fault?" she said. "He'd overlooked the promise of life. He suddenly saw it."

"Yes, I suppose so. What a good reason for not committing suicide. Ha, ha, ha" I laughed. "It's certainly a hell of a lot better than stopping the act because life's so unpromising because society's at fault. . . . Ha, ha, ha," I laughed again. Of course I would not tell the truth.

A Lonely Image

Soft Voices Pour
Cool Thoughts
Into My Mind.

They Speak Gently,
The Words are Not Clear.
But the intonation
Conjures Images
of Happiness.

There is a Song Being Sung
and The Sound of a Humble Guitar
Accompanies the Voice.
There is Laughter.

The thoughts turn into a
Simple Desire to be a part of
The Voices.

I Look into My Mind and
See the Soft Voices are
Strangers—Their words are
Happy Because I Believe they Are.

The Song is Sung and the
Guitar is Strummed
By a Record.
I want to be a part of
The Scene.

I can't—
I am sitting
Alone (with my thoughts)
in a Bar
With my drink!

Overheard in a Bar

been holding conversations
with the pictures on the walls
little men coming in through the keyhole
walking around in the middle of my suitcase
drinking witch hazel, bayrum, lilac vegetal
extracts, perfumes,
mothballs, and gingerale.
i smell like a cedar chest.
from the bottomless trapdoor of my nightmare
a Confederate general emerges
carrying white carnations for a headless woman.

GENE DENNIS

Memories of a Blackout

I came this way
once before,
but I don't remember
what I wore
when I lived in doorways
of skidrow days
and my heart
held horror shows
in the corridor.

Hours getting wasted
in waterfront bars
that used to lean
against the shoreline
railroad tracks,
tipping up Ripple
between the railroad cars.

Nothing left to amputate,
no bearings by which
to navigate.
Broken bladder,
leaking mind and
a prayer: for the next drink
to create a carnival and cauterize
the memory
of trying to sell
a snot-stained body
along North Beach curbs
on the hustle for another bottle
or the part of one.
Grateful the morning after
there were no takers
in this liberated zone.

Countless days
climbing the Matterhorn
on roller skates

while scavengers screeched
inside.
Defiling my own home,
begging to be left alone,
until I was.

My mind a wooden horse
kidnapped
from a mad carousel
and drugged with Dramamine
to soften the sickness
of seeing childhood dreams
come apart at the seams;
then revived
by the radical's drive
to dream again.
Playing the part
of God, Guru, and Guerilla
while leaving a snail's
trail of slime
across endless sidewalks,
haunted by the reflection
of hubcap eyes.
Forever swearing
between torrents
of brewer's piss
there would be no more
of this.

Agonizing weeks
or months
of trying to ride the wagon
and unravel the knots
inside.
Writhing in
a wordless sensation
resolved into an
excruciating
declension of tension,
finite and deafening.

The day always came
when it was impossible
to survive to see
the other side
of psychic pain
(or
seek out blue sails
in the sunset)
through sober eyes,
and I ran again
to the place of lies
and empty smiles.

Through it all
there was a child
who kept my heart alive,
incubated in his curious eyes,
chattering a leprechaun's lexicon,
protecting a spark of life
with sudden hugs and snuggles,
Breathing life
where there was no breath
Until I was given
the strength to see
the time had come
for a final choice,
and cried out
when there was no voice
and was heard
when there was only death
and was helped
when I thought there
was only me.

I struggled once
to name this healing force
until
the grassfields laughed
and said:
It really doesn't matter.

Longshore Joe

It took eight tries to get on my pants. Already weak from the countless spasms that wracked my body, I would climb from the bed, weak-kneed, and make another attempt. Though I had lain in bed for the entire long night, I was exhausted. The room in the Dominic Hotel was as small as a coffin, and I thought of it as such, in a city of exhilaration and activity to imagine myself lying dead, a sick, ugly body, bloated by booze. I am unable to smell, but others must gag. The room had a short bed with the sheets gray; I'd never put them out in time to have them changed. Only a narrow passage between the bed and the open closet—two dirty shirts and a bulky sweater, gravy- and wine-stained, that I had borrowed. The one container overflowing with soda cans of orange, grape, and rootbeer and bottles of Ballerina and Royal Gate vodka. Dozens of bottles scattered across the floor, many more shoved into the drawers of the only dresser. One cardboard box full of papers and clothes jammed. Like my life, the room was in shambles. The coughing started again—way deep from the pit of my stomache and each cough shook my body, trembling, spasms, tears, gagging. There was no food to vomit, I hadn't eaten in over seven days. The sweat slick against the dirt of my body, no bath for over two weeks. Each day a promise to bathe and so weak and fearful that I would fall into the tub or slip in the shower and lay there with a concussion or a broken leg—and once I was in the Eagle, and had had four or five drinks, and the shakes had subsided and the arrogance returned, I would forget the shower or the bathing.

On the eighth try, I managed to haul the pants up my legs, my balance so tenuous that I fell back onto the bed, squirming my body side to side to pull the pants over my hips. I reminded myself not to take the pants off. Though it was cold outside, the room was stuffy and without a window open for ventilation. I could not remember, but sometime in the night I had kicked the pants from my body. My heart pumped fast as a triphammer. I have high blood pressure, and I knew my pressure must be astronomical. I lay on the bed exhausted, my breath coming in short, wheezing gasps, always, on the edge of convulsive coughing. By raising my head, I could see small change on the dresser, not much and feeling into my pockets, one bill. Shakily pulling it out and looking, a lonesome five in a lonesome room. Get out to the Eagle and cuff some money in a place where my credit was near its limit. Days had gone without recollection. I didn't know what day it was, vaguely remembering borrowing money from the credit union over at the hall. I had signed a loan for $500 and actually received $200 in cash, and the fiver was all that was left. By weakly raising my head, I looked over the floor—but no such luck. For a gambler who lived on luck, at times my luck was miserable. My brother, who was a business agent for our union, the San Francisco Longshoremen, was away at a convention, and his wife was strictly a no-tap city as far as I was concerned. The image of a trapped animal returned, and with renewed strength I sat up on the bed and plowed through the bottles pouring the dribbles and hoping against hope that one bottle might accidentally hold a shot. Total—just barely enough to wet my tongue. The blood pressure pills were long gone, and the blood pounded in my head. One goal. Get up and out and get a drink.

Drinking in the bar put me under a double pressure. I didn't want to leave the bar. I had no place to go. People—even friends—were tired of seeing me. Tired of loaning me money or having me drink up all the booze in their house or talking all that ragtime talk of the past and the good old days, tired of the old stories, just generally sick and tired of a pest and in some ways a stranger who was on a different circuit and one that had only one direction—downhill. Mainly I couldn't go back to the room. If I had been able to sleep, it might have been OK, but not to lie there and look at the ceiling and the four walls in a room that was to be my coffin. The constant vision of my runaway wife. Christ, I couldn't be drinking over her. We hadn't slept together for the last five years, and the last two were miserable. Maybe one preferred misery over lonesomeness.

I ordered another drink. I had become unstable, and exhaustion pervaded my body. I could not for the life of me remember when I had last eaten. I knew that I stunk like a goat. In a land where every other wino stunk like a goat I was acceptable—nowhere else.

I had no money, nothing in the bank, checks bouncing all over the place. My credit was tap city.

Sunday—and the only bar open on the waterfront was Reardon's. I was sitting on a stool, and my heels were locked in the metal rung. Never had I been so weak, hands trembling, even my knees were shaking. They were talking of the night before. A dozen rats had run in through the swinging doors, run over the bar and the bottles to get at the Polish sausages. The customers banging at them with poolsticks, kicking at them, blood all over the floor. I tightened my heels on the rungs. I didn't have enough strength to kick them away. Christ—to find an open bar and this bullshit—rats.

"How big were they?" I asked.

"Big as dogs," the bartender answered.

He reminded me of an old tintype, hair plastered down, striped old-fashioned shirt. I knew him to be tough. A no-nonsense man who had done time in the joint. Good for a tap if he was in the right mood. Buy drinks out of his own pocket if necessary.

"Since they tore down all the warehouses and the piers, they're hungry as tigers." A black postal worker talking.

The bar was primarily for longshoremen, teamsters, postal workers, and a high collection of winos that filtered in and out, never trading over the bar but coming in for take-out bottles of wine. Only in and out, half-battered, sick-looking men with froggy voices.

"Gimme a vodka and orange juice," I said. "Light on the orange."

The bartender placed the drink before me. "Never have I seen the motherfuckers so bold. One ran clean along the bottles, and I just got out of the way. Looked like a battlefield."

"Any come in today?" I asked, my hands shaking as I reached for the drink.

The magic in a few drinks of vodka. The trick was to get the first ones down fast. Spill as little as possible. Get it past one's throat without gagging.

"Must of had a rough night," the bartender said, and he watched me suck the drink down. The knowing eyes focused on my face, the bloated face, and the fat, pudgy hands, fat as pork sausages.

"I'm not too loaded," I said. "Am I good for a tap?"

"Ten bucks—no more. We got bum checks a mile high, and the boss said no more checks."

"I don't mean a check."

"I know what you mean—but two of the checks are yours."

Rats and checks. By the fourth drink, my hands had calmed, and as I stood to go to the toilet my legs seemed steadier.

And now I was back in the room and prepared for the silent and paralyzing torturous passage to insanity or destruction. (Try as I might, I was unable to say "death.")

At night I saw the rats—hard to concentrate on them as the small angels spelled them off in relief. Small angelic girls with pouty girl faces and the curly golden hair and the straightup wings attached to their backs. My wife had been gone for over ten years and the loneliness didn't come after her departure; no, not until two years ago. We did not get along, and our last years together were a mess, but the mind has the ability to dispel bad memories. Often when I thought of her recently it was Easter. We were on the Marina Green, and my daughter had a Japanese kite high in the sky. My wife was in a pale lemon dress and a floppy white hat and had a white parasol. She had legs that were show-stoppers—even made old men turn around—and we walked hand in hand, and the girl held my other hand, and as we ate my wife's leg brushed mine and it was intentional. I lit her cigarettes for her, and the girl blew out the matches and we were together like a communion. Often she lapsed into silence and her eyes sparkled and we knew, she knew, I loved her, and I knew that she knew, and whatever was in my face and the pressure of my hand on hers told her we were one and the church ceremony that had united us made us one and our daughter was a replica of our love and our passion. And after we ate in the Basque retaurant we danced to the accordion player, and he played *La Paloma* over and over, and the girl sucked on a rootbeer with a straw, and the glow in her face responded to our movements as we faked a tango . . . *La Paloma* over and over again.

Between drinks, as if I were on a merry-go-round, the constant flood of images, the blanket tight about my neck, constantly cold, shivering, brushing cobwebs from my face, no longer able to discern the imagined from the real. Perhaps the images from the past were as unreal.

My wife had been a good dancer, wrote exquisite poetry, was Portuguese, and her father had been a longshoreman. He was dead and out in Holy Cross. I vaguely remembered him on the job, at the wedding, and his bulk-shouldered pride whenever he looked at his daughter. Her somber, flashing eyes her best feature. The slender legs and the cara delgada (slender) face and the hair, tarantula black and the black eyes dark as ink. Danced the Greek dances in the Minerva with an impenetrable face, a mask, as she danced the jaunty, lilting steps. She had no temper in the early days of our marriage and not even after her first hospitalization. Her sulkiness, punctured by deep, despairing moods, increased with her fear of the endless rounds of operations.

After the child was born, she went to see a therapist. Our priest suggested the therapist. Our sex life had never really been satisfactory, straight sex, one position only, the stiff uptightness of a virgin as she was the day I married her. The original intention, the reason she visited the therapist, was to locate emotionally, psychologically, the cause of her severe headaches. After each visit to the therapist, I found a new woman in bed. Unerringly, after each session kinky stuff, often masochistic. I asked no questions, and she gave no answers. Her ability to wear black and white underclothes and invest them with a mood of wild passion. After her therapeutic visits, her headaches were no longer a point of discussion between us. We went to mass every Sunday, and finally I quit wondering—how can you do anything wrong with your own wife? And then she took to wearing no underclothes, and when I came home I would shower, and we followed the ritual of dinner, kisses on the couch, while the child watched TV and the late wild nights—and what shatterings!

And the ribbings from my brother: "Don't you ever go out and play cards on Friday any more?" I had been a great gambler, horse player, card player. "People will think you're square, going to the ball games and racetrack with your own wife. She must have the best-looking legs in the whole goddam city but Jesus Christ, you two will burn each other out."

And sure enough, we did but it took a long time. The epileptic dances in the late night became kinkier but all that was noticeable, except to my brother, was our love. She being a nontalker and a silent as a tomb. I volunteered no information.

Her lips were sensual and soft and her teeth nippy and bitty as she consumed me alive. I could hardly watch her nibble asparagus without getting a hard-on. At the same time her cooking improved. The nights we spent trout fishing, camping out, and lying in our sleeping bags on the cots, and she listened in silence as I pointed out the constellations to the girl—Orion, Cassiopeia. And the sunsets at the bench and the wild abandonment in the surf, caressing and rolling in the surf. The time under the trees in Muir Woods during the monumental rainstorm when my blue blazer shrunk. The Marina Green with me stroking atop her barely under the arcs of the headlights of the commuters going toward the bridge. I whispered, "This is insanity. We have a house and a bed only four blocks away!"

We turned each other on—no whips or tying up or swinging arrangements with other couples, none of that bullshit. Just the expansion of our love into the physical.

The rats and the little girl angels were back again and the snakes and the explanations necessary if I was to keep from going insane. Perhaps the not eating, the no food made me dizzy in the brain and unable to stay with a single thought and generally alcohol erased the blackboard of my mind, distributing the past into broken segments to be dispersed from the bridge into suicides of floating paper that kept one from going off the bridge on one's own

and should I in the room's darkness write a note explaining what I am to do if I am sure of what I am about to do, and after two more drinks the ones earlier were harder to get down and these with strawberry soda pop from the small fridge in the corner, vodka and soda pop, how crazy can one get, and what of the angels and the rats and the snakes and the tattoos and the vision of my wife in black panties and none of my dad who died in the famous mine disaster in the Mother Lode and the search for gold claiming those—those who—and my mom with her heavy way of walking buried up the hill in Jackson and dad deep in the mine locked in whatever secrets transpired in the tomb carbon darkness—never the figure of my wife, never Maria Teresa—the entire feel of her as a presence, some gypsy-conjured mood, some vodka-induced hypnotic trance envisioned from the corner of my eye and never sure—somewhat terrifying—the longshoremen, living mixed with the dead—a floating of deadheads bobbing alongside the ships and squashed by vans falling from cranes and heads torn asunder. Asunder, I don't even know the word *asunder*. The vast army of the dead crowding the corners of the room—repeat after me—a hallucination is a temporary dysfunction of the reticular network-like activating mechanism of the brainstem, images that don't belong together are brought together. A hallucination is exaggerated psychologically by apprehension. Of what am I apprehensive, and apprehensions are unnamed fears, and of what am I fearful? Certainly not death or my divorced wife or the waterfront, and I am not fearful of love or rejection or hate or resentment or even self-pity for that matter—why snuff out one's life—the lack of hope? To awaken and face each day, and the bleak and despairing landscape. I'm not an existential being, not a child of those dark, moody philosophers or even novelists or Doctor Menninger's dictum—drinking is a form of suicide—a vicious circle. One drinks to ease the pain of despair and not to commit suicide. And drinking lulls one, anyway. What does Menninger know of black friction tape placed over the window glass, trembling fingers to shut out the light of life, and how it might be a tunnel of dimness like a mine or a coffin or associated with the blackness of a woman's hair, and what did I have left of her but a few pubic hairs in the wallet behind the driver's license, and how nutty can one get. Black dim tape darkness mine tunnel coffin hair Maria Teresa black despair lack of hope and apprehension of unnamed fears but with a continuity that may or may not be self-perpetuating and cause apprehension. I know that I am in reality, and the visions do not make much sense, and they are not uncomfortable, unless they are terrifying, and how could my dad or Maria Teresa be terrifying? And why the continuous flood of sensual memories? How unusual when I commonly never thought of that part of our life and was not a victim of fantasy or did not overdream—was this all a dream and my spasms started again and when I was not able to control the coughing and the wretching, the shuddering of the body into convulsions, this was no dream.

The one way of clearing my mind, stop the merry-go-round of would-haves, should-haves, could-haves, might-have-beens . . . pour three or four ounces of vodka or gin into the glass, no longer any need for ice, pour in some mix and down the hatch. Feel it go past my throat into my stomach, the warmth and the hit, the pervasive contact with all my senses, the deadening of nerves. The periods of reprieve shorter and shorter. Another glassful. Where would it all end? The rats had come up on the bed, and the angels were toying with my hair, and I began to sweat profusely. Once rising from the bed and a complete nothing. Senseless for how long? I had fallen on the floor and my fingers were bruised, and I lay propped against the side of the bed. The front of my pants completely wet. Had I poured booze on me, upset a glass, or was it urine? I had never had a convulsion and was not sure that I had one now. Cautiously rising from the floor and crawling under the covers, breathing heavy, only the caressing fingers of sleep carrying me on an endless river, drifting and bobbing. And it happened again, at least twice by my count and my ribs banged and a lump on my head and the sudden loss of consciousness making me paranoid and I was at the law of diminishing returns, when alcohol no longer did what it was supposed to do. The sudden creepy and tightening corner that I had driven my life to. The vacant feeling of meaningless. What of my daughter, and Monte, too? There was the sense of caring, the band of blood, the locked concept that we were of the same mother and father. I was upset, the maudlin tears running down my cheeks. One more big glassful of Scotch, with a bare sprinkle of soda, just enough to disguise the medicinal taste. I could not stop the tears. Our Lady of Guadaloupe. My hands shook violently, the taste of blood in my throat and then blackness. I passed out.

Women

Rakela
my grandmother ran the show
imprisoned by language
burdened by petticoats
partially immobilized by a stroke
she beat the drum, the family danced to
my recurrent dream
a black bowling ball, rolling and
picking up speed
my anguished cry, only to be caressed
as i begged her never to let me die
never to let me be taken away
no, you will never die, never be taken away
it sounded so beautiful in that baltic tongue
so reassuring, so placating
i knew i was never to die, for i was
her streak of sun, her bloodline
beyond the grave.

Henrietta
my mother in a rocker
warming herself in the stucco and
california sun, her fingers bent and twisted
arthritic stalks
faded dress all ribbons and rhinestones
when i close my eyes i see
a beautiful girl with long and attractive legs
shingled hair a deep brown that glows in the sun
mother, what is it like in the sightless brocaded coffin
mother, i grieve for you
light a candle every day.

Dorothea
my slender wife in a pale lemon dress
and white parasol
easter on the marina green
she loved baseball and the racetrack
so out of keeping with her cool isolated manner
i call her *reina de los espejo,* queen of the mirrors,
as i try to capture a true and accurate image of her
all i ever see is her reflection
in court, her screams of
what i already knew
that i am imprisoned in the past
only interested in illusions of my family
that were not even true.

Linda Raquel
my daughter's shy smile
and girlish laughter
she stuttered in grammar school
as she moved cautiously into womanhood
the band of steel that gives her strength
drive and determination
comes from a transmission line
of blood, her ancestors
nomads on some bleak and icy plain
breathing frost, watching the midnight sun
she is a watcher, a checker
she watches the sea, insects, touches leaves
when i listen to her girlish laughter
i know that i am never to die
for she is my streak of sun
my bloodline beyond the grave.

A One-Night Stand

A week-long run
of autumn sun
and a paycheck fattened
by a six-day loading job
said it was time
to feed a fantasy
and take myself out to dinner.

First: a bubble bath
by candlelight;
a jazzman's
vibraphonic tale
on the record player.

Then a moment wrapped
in terrycloth,
feeling muscles forget
the strain of stumbling
on steel pipe all day.

I chose my clothes
from thrift shop treasures
and stepped out
somewhat studly,
feeling shy
but proud to be with me.

The restaurant worked
a nearby neighborhood
with candles
and Italian smells,
imported posters
and domestic wines.

I savored a special salad
dressed with just the right amount
of too much garlic.

On this daring night
there was no newspaper
to occupy my eyes.

The waitress smiled back.

Everything
inside my head
was geared way down
to let the quiet linger.

A forgotten joke
about a pregnant pig
pushed a giggle
past my throat.
The calm came back
before the blush was gone,
in time to pay the check
with the flourish
of an exaggerated tip.

Back home
the night light lit
the lonely linen sheets
with amber promises.
It felt so good
to make love with someone
who knew
my every move.

Dear Sally

We walked
a Mendocino mile
on the beach
today,
the child and I.

Over rocks,
under driftwood caves;
sand fleas piping
in the spray.

We watched
receding waves
give birth
to afternoon tidepools;
lost a game
of tag
with giggling foam
in the folds
of the rippling surf;
rolled in the sand
sat on a log
dove in the dunes
and died with a smile
spreadeagle
in the depths
of the fog.

Salt settled
in the corners
of my eyes,
sand burrowed
through my socks
and nestled
between my toes.

The child
moved away
to play.
My heart found yours
and there was
fire
in the sand.

Waiting for My Wife

Hours staring at paintings
Eating in museum cafeterias
Running through surrounding parks,
Same paths taken by a famous longshore philosopher.
Waiting for my wife.
Alone/Reaching vista points
Chasing ships away from the bay
with my eyes
tired of the slab-cold containers,
steel boxes, cyclone fences, block cement freeways.

Monet's watery call.
Luminous colors, ever-changing dimensions,
Waterlilies, ponds, small boat ideas.
Mind struggling with higher forms.
What gives unity?
Who still speaks with clean breath
from lake and pond, from changing colors,
the meeting of land and water—
Across the sea of time?

One wave after another
turning under. Great subjective sea
moving forward
I study the charts of time,
Sanskrit scrawled on the beaches
between Om and Revolution.

The tideland/border of life.
Fight of microorganisms,
constantly rearranged by sea and wind.
Where the sea, in a blackout,
foams forward to the land.
Where the artist, exhausted,
Reaches into waves,
Directing water around and
through his fingers.

Remembering:
Guard the secrets
Constantly reveal them.

Women in satins and silk
shimmering like the sea
with Beaux Artes Degrees
balancing ideas in the museum
Sifting through spaces
in conversations.

One more look at a Monet.
There it is, against the luminosity,
the notes,
remote, cool, speaking of slender shadows:
Sibelius and Davis (Miles).

My wife's passion voice I want
Silibant, intricate.
She stands before me,
Refined from argument,
turned to pleasure,
deeply beautiful—
her air,
Sudden and ripe,
Heavy with release.

Generation Gap

Father

Remember '34?
>   For What?
Remember those that Died?
>   Where?
Rember the Gas?
>   Why should I?
Remember how We starved?
>   How Come?
Remember the Bayonets?
>   Did they use them?
Remember—I was there—I was one of them.
>   And What did you Accomplish?
Remember—We organized the Unions—
>   So—what did you get?
Remember—you don't remember! You were too young to know!

Son

I am not too young to know—I Remember '69. Do you?
>   For what?
Remember those who died?
>   Where?
Remember the Gas?
>   Why should I?
Remember the Bayonets?
>   Did they use them?
Remember—I was there—I was one of them.
>   And what did you accomplish?
We tried to make a better World.
>   So did We.
You failed.
>   So did you.
You failed me.
>   You failed me.
We failed each other.
>   I can't talk to you when you don't remember.
I can't talk to you when you don't listen.

Did You See My Father Die?

Born a Leo,
Cancer was his
rotting sign.

Build of a lumberjack,
soul of a sailor,
brains of a bolshevik,
dreams of a savior;
crucified by coronaries,
tormented by tumors.

Tobacco-stained smiles.
A snarling slap
during drunken interludes.
Bear hugs across
the funny papers
on Sunday morning.

Standing in the
luminous hospital hallway
I saw him begin to crumble,
but never saw him
fall.

Thoughts on My Mother's Death

My dawn began as a pregnant seed in a peachtree town.
"You'll see, someday I'll be dead!" she said.
On a hot-red, flame-streaked day; waiting for my
mother's womb to relax enough for me to settle in.
"You'll see, someday I'll be dead!" she said.

My mother's coffin lay open and her powdered white
undertaker's face belittled her death.

I was born 12:01 AM on the 7th day of the 7th month
of the year nineteen hundred and twenty four—in
Cleveland, Ohio. "You'll see, someday I'll be dead!"
she said. I don't know if there was a moon. I was
a breach birth, and bear the marks of the forceps on
my forehead.

My father rushed to kiss her one more time.
His tears stained the whiteness and ran down her cheek
as if she, too, mourned her death. They closed the lid.

I was five, living in Pittsburgh, Pa. A cop killed my
dog Nellie and my mother took him to court and got him
fired from the force. "You'll see!" she said.

The funeral home was ten stories high. Like a hotel.
There were people pointing to my brothers and saying,
"She also has a son who lives in California." I didn't
tell them it was me. "Someday!" she said.

My hair at six was covered with bubble gum. I fell
asleep with it in my mouth. My mother cut my hair off.
Shorn of my locks I cried and cried and cried. "You'll
see someday!" she said.

Not a tear—not one when she died. Just a dry, parched,
pain wracked my throat. A fierce headache penetrated
through to my very being and a feeling of sadness
overwhelmed me. "I'll be dead someday!" she said.

At sixteen I went into the CCC. She kissed me goodbye.
And at seventeen I went into the Army. She rode with
me to Penn Station. I was sad and mad and glad she was
there. She kissed me goodbye. Her youngest was off to
war. All her children—three sons were off to war.
"Someday!" she said.

They closed the door of the hearse. The coffin's weight
was still in my hand.

"Mom!" I would say, "How many times do I have to
tell you not to call me at work!" and "Yes! I'll tell
the kids to kiss you hello when they see you! How's
Pop? The job's OK. Mom, I've got to go—the boss
is waiting. I don't know when we'll see you next.
It will be soon! Yes I love you—now please—I've
got to go!" "Someday I'll be dead!" she said.

The hearse pulled away. We were lined up—so many
to a car. I was in the first car with Pop and my
brothers. We joked about riding in a limousine and
what it was like to have a chauffeur. "Someday!" she said.

The ride through the city was unreal. It was a perfect
day for a funeral. A New York winter/fall sun filtered
through a cloudy haze that made people, buildings, trees
and things ethereal. "You'll see!" she said.

We fought over the piano—that someday is here.
She fought with my dad—that someday is here.
She yelled at the kids—that someday is here.

The hole was six feet deep covered with fake green grass.
A bower was formed by a tree. She carried me for nine
months. I only had to carry her three minutes.

The life that gave me life—that brought me into
being was now gone. The "someday" that frightened me
to tears as a child was here. The wind blew gently
as I said goodbye and it is only now—many years later—
I acknowledge her death—and my love for her.

"You'll see!"—so she said and so I did!

For My Grandfather (Whom I've Never Seen) and My Father on His Eightieth Birthday

Grandfather, is this really a blood ritual,
a salt tango?
You and I separated by decades,
Never knowing each other.
A trace of ancient remembrance, blood debt,
dim spaces between night sails.
You are imprisoned in my memory
my Long Kesh memory.
Jailor ideas, that's why you left Ireland,
Swiping of feet, beat to repression,
Dedalus wings of sailcloth
bound in this harping, craven
Long Kesh memory.

North Atlantic, ice flows, WW I.
You ship out of retirement—veer from U-boats
Silent balance of cold and water—you sleep
Night-lead sleep, dream-swarming gulls
with bled-white wings.
Son of Tara, brother of Brendan,
the sleep of sailors and time itself.

Awakened by changing rhythms.
To the engine room, condenser blows
You are welded to the boiler plates,
catwalks, or . . .

Now, 100 years since you sailed round
the world with your father,
I have worked the ships of the
Romantic Past: *Adirondack Victory,*
Irish Spruce, Perseus,
Hakone Maru, Vishva Pradesh,
Vladimir Mayakovsky.
Weak-light, ice-flow, wind-torn days
checking cargo in holds. The salt chemistry,
moon pull, tidal call I share with you
on late night bays; the channels to the sea,
opening to deep water, past
the tideland struggle for life.

Your son is eighty today.
He too of the long memory.
Your continuation, the brazen-winged survivor
who strengthens the shrouds, a watcher,
a wanderer, a worker, a poet
son of Cuchulain
who battled the tide.
We search for open water. Oh Halcyon days!
A jailor rattling his keys
engaged by the shaman, seanachie sea.

He tells me salty stories of you.
Brown headland dying gold orb of sun
the plumes of surf
your sailcloth wings.

The Larger World:
Gathering in the Nets

Urban Renewal: Icarus Descending

Flying from the memory
of an old longshore hall
surrounded by the black glass buildings
garbled reflections
of another city
buried by boutiques
shrouded in crepe de chine.

Death pallor of wax museums
coffee house-motel-tour bus hallucinations
A pier where I sorted cargo
Sling-loads of coffee,
lead ingots—
a black arsoned hulk remains.
The crab and shrimp boats
forever marooned
in the Bay.
Pleasure craft docked
near-phantom images
resurrected to sell:
postcards, moccasins,
cheesecake, harpoon hamburgers,
and automated longshoremen's lunches.

Yes yes yesterday yet I fall
from the grace of fashion shows
begging musicians,
displaced workers
tap-dancing to any tune
They languish mid the maze
entrapped by Minos and his
bullish stockmarket son
amassing tribute.

My grandfather went down in the Atlantic
for you, Minos
I never say him
My father in frontline trenches, WW I,
and at home, the longshore strikes
He is the survivor,
the continuator,
Far from the sea, far from the sun.

Your winding buildings
Your labyrinth
Your all-consuming Minotaur
Your vulgar glamour
Red gore on golden horns.

Yes yesterday yet I fall
Among dead men
raising nets
Nets around the city
Teaming with goods and fish and life.

Lust and money
Knife slashing edges
The sting of salt and blood
Tremors of light, convulsing foundations.

I arise on tolling bells
Reclaiming thermals
above the fog
at the beltline of TransAmerica.
Grasping the last-gasp beauty burned in the sun.

Blood memory strained through crepe de chine.
Light refracted from the past
rising in dim pools on the Bay.
Secretaries straining in downtown days.
Ariadne with red-lacquered fingernails
Sister to Phaedra scratching the black glass
garbled reflections
of another city
Crying in blood debt:

Sailor and longshoreman, grandfather!

Father far from the sun
I saw you
the old man on air
an awkward bird
As I grasped agasp
at this fatal miscalculation
I have fallen
deeper
than your expectations.

Did ever winds of high convictions
rattle upon young Icarus?
But it is difficult
to
descend
upon new monstrosities
without wings.

KEN FOX

Fighting Windmills:
A Fantasy of a Knight and His
Dragon

In the deep dank night
The Widget comes to grouse around my house.
It likes to wrap its slimy paws round my head
And squeeze me like a melon ball;
Till I go running, screaming down the hall
Tearing at the suckers on my skull!

I dig my nails into its damp, toady flesh
And feel its body writhe and slither
'Neath my grip.
We sing a duet of cacophonic shrieks and moans
And I regale the air with epithets in primordial tongue
Beknownst only to the Widget and to me!

We taste each other's sweat and blood and glory in the gore
As we fight some more. He seems to like this part the most,
And I play a most gracious
And entertaining host!

The moment he is sated he relinquishes his grip
And I grab his slimy tail like it was a whip;
And I spin him round and round my head till he screams
And cries, in dreadful tones, "I am dead—I am dead!"
Then I fling his slimy, sinewy body through the air
And I yell "All's fair, all's fair, you bastardy, reptilian,
freak! Now you can go back to your lair
Bloodied, bowed, and meek!"

The dawning sun glistens in the puddles of our blood
And one beam pierces my somnambulant eye
And I realize I didn't die! I didn't die!
I've got one more day on this blasted piece of sod
To make my way; and to drink another tankard or two.
Any maybe, if my luck holds out, I'll pitch a bit of woo!

Dare I say, I hope, with all my might,
Tonight, when I lay me down to sleep,
That miserable stinking lizard
Will not come grousing round my house again!
For if he does I'll show him who's master here,
Have no fear!
For I'll quickly grab his slimy tail
And dash him 'gainst the wall!
It will be his turn to go running,
Screaming down the Hall!

The Year They Invented Poor People

that winter stepdad lost his job
people became thinner
their eyes worried
thinking of the crash
steelmills shut down
streets shabbier
shuffle of panhandlers
in front of the theater
a woman in evening gown and tennis shoes
... looking for fun, mister?
as if there was any fun left anywhere in the world
as if some magician had plucked four out of five cars
off the streets
no butter, steaks, oranges
no coffee, tea, or milk
tailormade cigarettes had vanished
two people committed suicide
in our building in one week
they didn't even know each other
an elderly woman who plugged the keyhole
the gap under her door
turned on the gas
the hungarian,
goulash cooking on the stove,
when he did his dive
from a side window
head first.

mom made friends with bonnie
a beautiful redhead
teeth white as pearls
saucer blue eyes
innocence and candor
fragile wonder of her complexion
a pale texture that didn't take to the sun
a girl who with a little luck
might grace the footlights for ziegfeld

or a mansion on lakeshore drive
a poodle on her lap waiting for daddy
a big sugar daddy
magnate of a foundry
owned a steelmill or two
but bonnie had no luck
not many sugar daddies around
she married norman
a brakeman on the railroad
who wore baggy pants and chewed tobacco
and was fifty years old
but had a job
and had his pleasure
playing horseshoes and banging bonnie
so they came, one after the other,
seven kids in a row
she remained intact outside
... how wonderfully bonnie holds up
mom said
sag and stretch of what is inside
one day she collapsed
blood oozed from
her womb, uterus, vagina, kidneys
the ambulance took a long time to come
and made no difference
as she lay rigid
staring at the ceiling.

stepdad's car in front of the house
had no gas so it never moved
like bonnie it collapsed
tires sunk to the rim
iron fenders rusted
windows broken
people drank kerosene, sterno, rotgut hooch
starved, became tubercular
pneumonia carried them to the grave

bitter bayonet of wind
icedriven
riddling the threadbare clothes
hours tracking a scrawny pigeon
eating sparrows i regarded as friends
rat stunned on our kitchen table
as i beat it to death with a bat
excited by the blood
around the city i smelled the blood
as we waited
teeth clenched, stomachs empty and tight
bloodstained, exhausted
we waited.

KEN FOX

A Letter From a G.I. To a Vietnamese

I Watched a Child Die—
Her Arms and Legs
Burned to a crisp by Napalm.
Her eyes exuded Pus instead
of Tears.
The Plastic Bow Clip on her head
was Welded to her Scalp
and there was No Hair.

The Odor of Burnt Flesh
came out of her—very—dying—breath—
For she Was Burned Within As Well.
Death was a matter of minutes away.
I waited—wondering how much of what
I felt could be put into words.
Would anyone believe me?
Or would it be—That what I See
Would Have to Remain With Me!

I sat Down—Not too far away—
To Ponder over What I had Seen.
Then I Heard what Sounded like
A whimper and there—
A Small Woman crouched
Next to the Child's Body.
A Moan of Horror shook her tiny frame.
The contortions of sorrow forced
Her Arms and Head to move in an
Awful Way.

She Picked the Body Up
And tore her blouse Apart
Then put her warm, Milk-Filled Breast
to the Mouth of this once
Living Being—and Rocked—and Rocked
And Rocked—And Rocked
What more Can I Say?

YOU look now with my eyes—
for I wonder What you Would Say—
If At That POINT
YOU WERE ORDERED TO KILL HER!
I Heard the Words and tried to form my lips to say
"HOW CAN I!"
Instead I said
"Yes Sir!"
Would you believe this?
Would you Understand?
Could you Understand?

HAH***MAN***LISTEN
The Captain Said
KILL HER
"This is a War Zone—No Civilians"
MAN—THIS IS A WAR ZONE
A WAR ZONE
I CAN**KILL LEGALLY**

I felt a profound wave of Sorrow—
Tragic Eyes looked up at me—
Tears Flowing—
The Man Said—"Kill her for your Safety"
"She'll tell the enemy where you are Going—
Kill Her for your Safety—**Kill Her**
THAT'S AN ORDER!"
I looked at her and before my eyes she
Changed into a Bitch with a Dead Pup—
I had to change her into something more
Killable—

I shot the Child in the Head Knowing
She was Already Dead—The woman looked at the
Bullet Hole and then at Me—and with a feeling
of Utter Despair—I put a bullet between Her
Eyes, too—*THIS IS A WAR ZONE*
I*ME*CAN KILL LEGALLY

They tell me it's Patriotic to Kill—
They tell me it's the right thing to do—TO KILL
They tell me if I don't Kill Them they will KILL me.
The Hole Oozed blood—both bodies fell to the Ground—
The breast dripped a mixture of Dirt
Blood and Milk

CAN ANY GOD**ANY GOD AT ALL**EVER—FORGIVE ME

None that I know—Sorrow—None
Feeling—None
Who am I!

I write to you—A total Stranger—in the hopes
that you will Hear Me!
**I KILLED YOUR MOTHER—YOUR SISTER—SOMEONE
IN YOUR FAMILY**

I KNOW I DID—I KNOW I DID

I'm Sorry

The Party

People sit around in a
Circle of their minds—
Each one touching each one
Carefully.
Words Encounter Words
and change into thought
and then back again to
A word—sometimes
A Smile—A Tear or
Laughter!

There is a back and forthness
Give and take—
A Multileveled Game
of Overt Covertness
Played with Sexual
Oohs and Ahs
As a Player
Makes a Point
Below the
Navel.

Minds Turn and Bodies React
To Each new Wave
of Assertiveness
And Each Player Dances
With the Thought
and then tries
To Pass it On!

Little Encounters of
Sensuality are made with
Singular Raised Eyelidded
Winks or Jutted Breasts
or Knee to Knee
Contact—Subtle
only to the
Participants—
Not to the
Beholder

Sensory Perception Floats
Through a Bath of
Wine, and Libidinal
Interaction
Makes the Room
Warm, Soft, and
Round.

Lights Glow in Dilated Pupils—
Relaxed Bodies Cushion
Each Other. Thoughts
Not Verbalized are
Stored Away.
Syllables of
Happiness
Make a
Gentle Bed
for the
Minds.

Nigh Draws the Night.
Thoughts of Pillow
Comfort
Create an Aura of
Goodbye.
People Leave in
Lingered
Laughter.
The Party's
Over!

Quartet

Four—Sat in a Circle of Sound—
Smooth Bowed Arms
Moved with Pizzicato Ease—
over Double-Stopped Strings—
Fingertip phrases Leaped High
for a moment of life—
Aura of One
Merged Four.
Their Blend
Accentuated
By Pulse
made
a
Stream
of
       Allegro
             thought
                    Flow.
Mind Cells Gathered
By Sensual Sound
Absorbed by Passion
Released an Elixir of
Euphoria—
High Chromes and
Delicate Pastels
Mingled with their
       Aural Counterparts
             and
                this
                    Weaving Tapestry—

Created a Harmonic Balance within
Musician and Listener Alike—
They Merge into One—
Passionately Embraced by the
Goddess of Sound.
Each Theme broadens the Horizon—
Pastoral Splender Emerges—
Drawn on Long Bows of Filigree Thought.
Broad Strokes of Imagery
Fill the Air with a Pleasant Afternoon.
Songs of Conversation in
Four-Part Harmony
Create a
   Sense of Well-Being
                 Minds at Ease
                       Draw Sunset
                             Into Each Bow
As The Final
         Chord is
              Played.

Concert Artist

I think of what it must
Be like to lift a Bow
and upon
One Stroke
Change
the
Plastic Placid
ConcreteBlock
Artificial-leather-lined,
Mink-Coated Chair
First Row
Center
Auditorium
into
A
Sparkling   Dazzling
Murcurial
Orb
of
Spinning Webs
And
Mountain Tops
Of
Flowing Streams
And
of
Deep Chrome Chasms
Split By
Pale
Pastel
Skies!
I
Often
Wonder
What
It
Must
Be
Like!

The Return of Vaudeville

My son Jason said . . . success at sixty
the stage is dark
the curtain is down
the audience has gone home
the lost, the beat, and the hippy
generations have vanished
and a little fat man
smoking a short cigar
and carrying a handful of poems
comes onto the podium.

An Eclipse

I heard (saw) a sky full of Thunder
Turn into a single
Drop of
Rain
When the Earth passed between
Man's Mind and the
Sun

In Search of La Cruda

Jeremy sat sideways on the train seat slicing a four-pound avocado. Don was slumped in the seat behind him. The jungle swept by in waves of green and brown as we rattled and rumbled toward the Mexican coast. Dun-colored clouds of train dust poured into the car through the open windows.

"Hey, Sam, you asshole," yelled Don, "for this shit you pulled me out of Vesuvio's? Well, fuck you and your trains and your buses and the bugs and the warm beer, FUCK YOU!" He threw his dead beer bottle out the window and staggered down the aisle unzipping his fly. Before he reached the bathroom at the front of the car, clear drops of fresh beer piss began to dribble down into the dust. "And fuck you, too!" he shouted at the john door as he lurched inside the fly-filled cubicle and slammed the door—slammed it twice before it held shut.

Don was right in a way: it wasn't his trip. It was mine and Jeremy's. I looked over at the giant avocado, dissected and glistening by Jeremy's thigh. He picked up three eight-inch slices, tucked them between the lips of a chunk of bread, and passed them to me across the aisle. We smiled. I was glad the car was empty, except for an elderly American couple who never looked up from their *Sunset* magazine.

We weren't that young ourselves. Don's on the near side of forty, with a heavy booze trip on his tail after shipping out for nine years. Jeremy hit forty last October and split from his old lady and kids on Thanksgiving. At thirty-two, I'm the kid, with much college and two marriages behind me. Way behind.

"Sometimes I wonder," said Jeremy, "if we're doing the right thing, coming down here like this. I mean, well, for six months you and me have been planning to go all the way to the Yucatan and climb the ruins and get lost in the mysteries of the Mayans. And now, just because of some bullshit hangup at work, we've had to cut it short and settle for a week or so on the beach. I don't know if I'm up for this. It leaves me a little empty."

The avocado slid slowly down my throat. I felt the tufts of bread pull against the slimy sweetness of the fruit. Jeremy doesn't usually say that much at one time.

"Hey," I said, "would you do me a big favor and go see if Don passed out or something? I mean, that fucker's been drinking for two days, ever since we hit Guadalajara, and he's never spent more than three minutes in the head since I've known him."

Jeremy nodded and got up. As he unfolded from the seat he reached into his hip pocket and handed me the half-empty bottle of tequila. The other half we'd killed back at the station. I watched Jeremy's back muscles roll with the train as he moved cautiously down the aisle. I drained the bottle and felt my gut climb halfway up, gasping for air. Jeremy came back, smiling around the lips while his eyes frowned.

"Don's acting a little weird," he said, his head wiggling a little. "He's crying. He says he drowned a fly."

"His own?"

"No, asshole," said Jeremy, "he says he missed the bowl and pissed all over some flies on the floor, and one of them never got up."

"Did you see it?"

"Yeah," said Jeremy, "but it looked OK to me. I told Don that but he started crying again."

The train crawled around a curve, and suddenly we were suspended over a three-hundred-foot gorge. A river pushed against its banks beneath the tropical sun. Someone's bedsheets were spread across a crop of boulders to dry in the heat. Then they were gone, and a pulp mill grew on the far bank and vomited milky suds into the crystal current.

"Look, partner," I said, passing Jeremy the dregs of the bottle, "I know this isn't the trip we planned. I know this isn't the trip or adventure I wanted. But here we are, grimy and half drunk and on our way to some beach neither of us has ever seen before. It's different, but it's still an adventure, and I want some more booze."

Jeremy pulled his pack down from the rack above the seats and got another bottle out of the secret pocket beneath the top flap.

"Thank you," I said, twisting the fresh cap until the seal popped. "I think we've got to shift gears and get into *this* trip, or else we'll never feel like we left the docks in San Francisco."

It was getting dark. We heard an echoing cry of exultation from the john: "It *is* alive! ItisitisitIS!"

"Oh, shit," said Jeremy, "now he's going to be Mother Nature."

Jeremy was right. Don smiled and giggled and touched tree trunks all the way from the train to the bus and up the coast to our hotel on a wayward beach that had somehow eluded the plastic hotels of Puerto Vallarta to the north, and the more muted congestion of Manzanillo to the south.

It didn't take us long to get the wild shits. I got straight after three days. Jeremy and Don had tightened up by the second.

"Brother Sam," said Don the morning of the fourth day while my ass was still twitching, "we found out where the whorehouse is. You ready?"

"I'm ready."

We spent the day chasing a red frisbee on the beach and floating on our backs in the water drinking beer and trading tales of other whorehouses. We began the evening with a royal tequila sunset. Equal parts vintage tequila and one setting sun. We ate under the stars: fish pan fried in garlic, oil, oregano, and chili powder. The cook, a majestic woman with broken fingernails and cracked lines across her cheekbones, poured a salsa of onion and tomato over our plates.

"Enough. Enough, enough, enough," moaned Jeremy.

"Yes," said Don, trying hard to sound together, "enough. It is time to move on. To move in. To triumph."

Jeremey began his yoga breathing exercises. I watched the two of them through a fog trying to straighten up.

We held each other as we staggered down the street. Arms over shoulders. Hands around hips. Laughing as we stumbled into potholes, screeching as we wandered off the road into reptilian darkness. Finally we arrived at the magic door with sand in our shoes and eddies of booze and spit on our lips. Two raps and a cough and we were inside. A quiet place. Clean. Don paired up fast. Drinks came, and conversation. Me and Jeremy translating for Don.

"This is it!" cried Don, "I've found it! I'll never leave. This is the place! Now-and-forever!"

Jeremy kept trying to shrink away. I was right behind him.

"Fuuuck," said Jeremy. "Fuck him. I've had it with his drunken bullshit."

"I can't get into your anger," I said. "I know you're right—I just can't get into it."

"Fuck you."

I watched Jeremy walk away. He always moves the same, I thought. Slow, rhythmic, controlled . . . sensual. But he was gone. Don came back into the bar after his trip to the crib. Happy. Jeremy came back chewing on a mango. I noticed we were the only customers left in the place. I heard the door open and flinched at the sudden clatter of hard-heeled boots behind me. Jeremy looked past me over my shoulder and grimaced.

"Oh, shit," he said, trying to hold his words back behind his teeth, "the cops. Big ones."

By the time they reached our table they must have grown three feet. All three were huge. Skinny, but too tall and loaded down with pearl-handled automatics. They walked past our table, watching us without turning their heads, and went up to the bartender.

"I don't believe it," said Don, "stormtroopers in sombreros."

"Cool it, partner," said Jeremy. "You start any shit down here and it's all over. I mean o-v-e-r. Between us and for you. Hear me?"

"I hear, I hear."

The cops backed away from the bar, turned in tandem, and came over to our table. Two stood behind Don, flanking his chair. The third picked my shoulder to lean on. His pistol bumped my shoulder blade.

"OK, amigos," said the voice over my head, "you go now. Late. Time close up here."

Don leaned back and lifted his head until he was looking up between the cops. He turned slightly and draped one arm over his crossed legs.

"Sam," he said, still looking up, "tell me how to say pig. In Spanish. Tell me."

Ice formed in Jeremy's eyes. He leaned across the table.

"Is this the way you want to go, cocksucker?" he hissed. "Well, you go alone. *Puerco*. That's it, that's how you say it. Now do it, but do it alone—I'm splitting."

The hand was gone from my shoulder. I stood up and motioned I had to piss. The cop at Don's left waved me toward the john with a flick of his wrist. Jeremy was halfway to the door. I heard Don's chair move as he got up. I opened the john door.

"You know what we call you guys in the States?" Don was saying. I closed the door. He's crazy, I thought, and dumb. When I got back to the bar, they were gone. The bartender set a wet beer bottle on the bar and asked me to sit down. I was too fucked up to walk anyway. I held on to the beer and talked to the bartender. He bought me another beer. I felt good, like I belonged. It was a warm feeling.

"It is all right to leave now, my friend," he said.

I didn't want to go. Somehow holding on to that moment meant retrieving a lost dream of belonging someplace.

"Please, my friend," I said to him as he folded his white apron, "my throat is too dry for the journey. Surely you have thirst from the long hours. Here is two hundred pesos. Bring that bottle of Especial over here, and let us celebrate the end of the night."

He smiled and reached for the bottle and two glasses. I only remember taking the first drink. I woke up covered with wet sandpaper. Everything gritted and grated in the gray light. I was on the beach about a quarter mile from our hotel. An empty glass sat tilted in the sand beside me. I tasted whorehouse sewer in my mouth. Took off my shirt, socks, and shoes and slowly stood up, contemplating a salt-water bath. What I thought was a beached buoy was Jeremy.

"Good morning," he said, taking quiet delight in his eyes at my disorientation.

"Hi, guy."

"Goodbye."

I squinted at him: wearing denim cutoffs and a tan nylon windbreaker—no shirt, no shoes—carrying a snorkel and swim fins in his right hand.

"Where the fuck you going? Waddya mean, 'goodbye'?"

"I'm going diving off the point," he said tensely, "and then I'm packing and picking Don and his puke up off the floor and getting the fuck out of here. Going home. What are you going to do?"

I walked past him to the water, staggered by the soft sand sucking at my cuffs and feet. The water wiped out the world for an instant, washing me gray-cold and sickly sober. I sloshed back on the beach. Jeremy was still there, watching me. I didn't want to leave. I didn't have to be back at work when they did. But I was afraid to stay. Alone. I don't think I'd ever stayed anywhere alone for more than five days—but someone in my head kept insisting on staying for at least a month.

"Why don't you go to Merida?" said Jeremy. "Why don't you make that adventure anyway?"

"No. Not by myself. I think I'll stay here for a while. Kick back. Read. Maybe learn how to dive myself."

Jeremy shifted the snorkel and fins to his left hand, stretching seconds into minutes by adjusting the snorkel strap.

"Don't do it," he said, not looking at me. "Get that adventure together or come back with us. But don't stay."

"What?"

"Don't stay. Something's gone wrong for us here."

"For you, you mean," I said, getting angry. "You're upset about Don last night. Sure, he was an asshole. But it's over, and you guys are leaving. Don't get righteous about it."

"All you're doing is getting loaded all the time. You don't belong here."

"Fuck you! What do you know? You weren't there last night: me and the bartender, like partners. *Compadres.*"

"What's his name?"

I looked at Jeremy. The new sun turned the sand from grit to glitter.

"You know how it is," I said, fumbling around his words. "Like on the waterfront. Names don't mean anything."

"What you do does."

"That's why I'm staying. To do something I've always wanted to do: be a beach bum with no job or woman or television to get in my way."

"Just do it with style, Sam."

"Yeah."

"See you before we go."

"Yeah."

Jeremy walked down the beach. I was eager for a beer and slogged back to the hotel—really a small, freshly built, stucco horseshoe of rooms stuck between a bustling restaurant on the street side and a thatched veranda on the beach. Plaster-spattered workmen were still patching and painting the place. I dodged between makeshift scaffolding and went into the room. Don was a crumpled, snoring mess on the floor. I showered in cold water—the hot tap just made spitting noises—and lay down on my bed to rest, but Don smelled too bad. I pulled on a pair of polka-dot Mark Spitz dual-purpose bikini shorts and a pair of army fatigue cutoffs, being real careful not to bend over too far. Retread woven sandals creaked comfortably as I walked to the door.

Outside, three workmen cut tiles and exotic hardwoods in the patio. I turned away from them and shuffled down the plank walkway to the veranda. I sat down at one of the scarred card tables and jumped as my folding chair sank six inches into the sand. Caught the shy eyes of the kitchen girl and signaled for two beers. Pelicans were already patrolling the bay. Two shrimp boats rolled gently at anchor beneath a swarm of smaller birds. A blur of brown hands left the cold, wet bottles and half a lime on the table. I picked up one—quickly, so my hand wouldn't shake—and chugged it. My stomach settled enough so I could look around. A lean, tan, gray-bearded man in a swim suit sat three tables away, smiling at me.

"Hello," he said.

"Hello," I said, feeling my face close up against the stranger, the trespasser.

"You guys been having a good time?"

"Beautiful," I said, feeling the second beer turn me friendly.

"My name's Larry, Larry Whittaker."

"I'm Sam, Sam Waldron. Want a beer?"

"Sure."

Larry moved in when Don and Jeremy left. Getting someone to share the rent was the only way I could stay out the month, even though it violated every privacy principle I owned. We had agreed on the merger after Jeremy had come back exhilarated from diving, before we were all the way drunk. Jeremy started off friendly, curious about Larry's life as an air traffic controller, but quickly withdrew as the conversation got loudly slurred. I don't think we said goodbye again. I know I walked Larry down three dirt blocks to the hostel he'd been staying at to help him get his gear. When we got back, Don and Jeremy were gone. I didn't go look for them. Instead, Larry and I stepped over to the adjoining restaurant and drank a case of beer to celebrate his arrival. Days later, in a quiet moment, I wished I had left with them or at least made some meaningful gesture at their departure. Larry broke in with a suggestion I take him down to the whorehouse. I liked moving around town with him. He was quiet, easy-going, respectful of the people without knowing the language, and he liked to drink.

We were loaded when we got to the house. The place was loud

and friendly. The bouncer recognized me. The bartender didn't. Larry fell in love in five minutes. I spent most of the time negotiating a bribe for the management and the police to let Larry spend the night with his lady. The kaleidoscope of customers and women and music stopped when two of the ladies confronted me.

"Why is it you are here two times now and do not choose to come with us to kiss a while? Are we not beautiful?"

"Very beautiful," I said, smiling and thinking fast. "I can see I must apologize for the fact I am still pure and am saving myself for my forthcoming marriage."

I wasn't ready for the laughter and cheers I got—and the endless line of free drinks. Something was indeed holding me back. It bordered on believing I was part of the town, not the tourists, and therefore took the role of enthusiastic spectator.

The bartender kept away from me when I moved to talk to him. I tried to read his eyes as "The time we spent together was after hours, therefore illegal, and should not be acknowledged." Yet I also felt I had done something in the unremembered time to offend him. I left Larry tucked in for the night and went back to the hotel veranda with a bottle of tequila. I don't remember going to bed, but that's where I was when Larry woke me up in the morning.

"You better get up," he said, grinning, "Your friends from the shrimp boat will be around pretty soon."

"What friends?"

"Oh, shit—you *were* fucked up."

"No, I wasn't. I remember everything except getting into bed."

"But you don't remember coming back to get me because you said the bartender was going to kill me?"

My stomach knotted. I jumped out of bed holding my head and threw up in the new toilet bowl that wouldn't flush anymore. I poured half a glass of tequila and sat down on the bed.

"What else did I do?"

Larry was laughing. "You broke up some tables and tried to buy five of the girls to prove you were more man than anyone else there had ever been."

"Oh, fuck!"

"Well, you didn't do it. And I paid for the tables."

I tried to pay Larry back but he wouldn't hear of it. Said his part of the night more than made up for the expense.

"Besides," he said, not smiling, "I'm getting ready to leave anyway—so consider it a farewell present."

"Come on," I said, "you said you've got as long down here as you want. Aren't we having fun?"

"It's been fun," he said, "but I don't want to overdo it. I mean, I can't keep up with you."

"Hey, that's OK. I'll slow down."

"I don't think you can."

"Jesus Christ. All right. Leave. I'll find a way to pay for this place."

"I found you a new roommate," he said, throwing clumps of clothes into a vinyl two-suiter. "Nice guy. A Swede or something. His name's Thor. Met him on the beach this morning. He was going up the coast for the day and said he'll be back with his things tonight."

"Fine."

I drank the tequila and put on the fatigue cutoffs over the polka dot shorts that I didn't bother to take off anymore. I picked up the bottle while Larry was in the bathroom and went out past the workmen—who were now mortaring the patio tiles—down to the beach. I didn't see Larry again.

I took off the cutoffs and waded out into the water with the bottle, drinking from it as I stood watching the pelicans dive. I saw a dinghy pull away from the larger shrimp boat and waddle toward me over the water. There were three men in it. One was standing, waving at me. I didn't recognize him or the others and decided they were the men Larry had been talking about. I wanted to get out of the water and hide in the room but the dinghy was too close and head messages weren't reaching my feet fast enough.

Standing there in water up to my chest with an empty bottle in my hand, I had a sudden memory surrounded by colors and mariachi music: Me and Larry sitting at a round table—at the whorehouse or a restaurant in between—and sea-smelling rough-shaven men at the next table. Someone playing music, many guitars. An old, fat, short man with a moustache gets up from the other table and begins dancing. Then I am dancing with him, hugging him. Everyone is laughing. He fills my nose with fish stench.

The dinghy beaches just to my right as I piss into the water under the easy waves.

"Good day, Sam. How is it with you?"

"My head is bad."

"That is no surprise. We have come to tell you we cannot go with you for lunch to the house of the whores because our captain has a head that is also bad and a stomach that is worse. He says you are to return with us to the boat for a party of shrimp and beer as his guest."

I looked out at the boat, riding dark and low and dirty in the water. I saw myself tossed drunk and naked over the side.

"Please tell your captain he honors me with his invitation, but the curtain of a hangover is drawn between me and the world, and I do not wish to be sick and soil the table of your captain."

"Our captain expected as much and instructs us to inform you we will meet again when we return from the south in two weeks."

"I will be fortunate to be here and honored to meet again with you and your captain."

"Go with God, Sam."

"With God. Until then."

"Until then."

I turned away and dove under the water, holding my breath and the bottle until I thought both would break. When I came up again, the dinghy was back at the boat and pelicans were crashing into the water around me. I floated on my back until I realized the bottle was only filled with salt water and became afraid a pelican would puncture me in a feeding frenzy.

Back on the beach, I stepped into the cutoffs to walk to the store where now they kept my tequila wrapped and waiting. On the way I avoided the veranda where the patrón was holding his daily luncheon for a horde of friends, and relatives. He always made a big show of ordering the kitchen girls about as they cooked countless dishes and set the table—the card tables pushed together and camouflaged with a fine linen tablecloth. He never spoke to me when we passed on the patio or in the street.

Out of the corner of my eye, I could see the patrón was placing his guests around the table, using a three-gallon jug of golden, aged tequila as his director's baton. When all were seated he looked around, grunted in his fat, gray-headed way, and set the jug down in front of him at the head of the table. I pushed my eyes forward so I wouldn't get caught staring at the one ritual I had come up against where I felt clearly marked and treated as an outsider.

"Hello, Mr. American!"

I turned without choice to face the gravel echo of the patrón's greeting.

"Good afternoon, patrón."

"Will you come sit with us today?"

I dug for energy or excuse to move on.

"Please, Mr. American, we would be honored more deeply

than the table of a shrimp boat captain if you would sit with us."

The others smiled. One snickered. I smiled. They all smiled.

"I am honored to be asked to sit at the table of the captain of the town and the bay."

Nods were added to the smiles. I moved forward, knees moving stiffly, conscious my clothes did not fit with the white shirts of the men or the black dresses of the women. The patrón called for a chair for me to be placed next to him.

"You have been here for some time," he said.

"Yes."

"You like it here."

"Yes."

"You like the tequila best of all." Laughter. I twitched.

"No matter," he said, "so do I. Do you like the marijuana?"

"Only when there is not tequila."

He poured us each a full glass of the finest tequila I had ever tasted.

"I make this myself where the Federales cannot see. But this matter of the marijuana—do you know Americans here who would like to have some?"

I twitched again and nodded without thinking.

"Good. Then you will send them to me. I grow fine marijuana. Once the Federales came to burn my marijuana. I killed one of them. No police has the right to step unasked on the private land of an honorable man, true?"

"Truly," I said, watching him refill my glass to the top.

"They put me in prison for twenty years."

I looked at him over the rim of my glass.

"That," he said, smiling, "was two years ago." Laughter.

"You," I said, "are a man with a special calendar, perhaps?" Jackpot laughter this time.

"No, my friend, a very special bank account." He turned away from me and took over the conversation at the other side of the table. I tried to talk to the goateed man next to me, a math professor from Mexico City married to a cousin of the patrón, but he wasn't interested. I excused myself from the table over very mild protests from one or two of the others. The patrón simply nodded at my departure. Standing, I tried to say something idiomatic to impress the group, but fouled out as tequila and nervousness sabotaged diction and vocabulary so that what I said came out something along the lines of "My balls are in my ear." I ran away from there as fast as I could walk.

I reached the street feeling very alone. I walked along the curb with my hands rolled into fists and pushed deep in the fatigue pockets. Two drunk and dirty mariachis sat across the street on the curb sharing a bottle of beer. They saw me and waved and called me by name. I didn't know who they were and waved back. I kept walking toward my store, looking down at my legs—brown now like most of the rest of me. My stomach felt strange. I couldn't remember eating a regular meal since that whorehouse night with Don and Jeremy. I had tried to remember to shave every day, but the last day or two it just didn't seem to matter. I walked past the little tortilla factory that scented the whole town at dawn and again at the end of siesta time. A dozen women and children were already lined up for the small brown tortillas they turned out. One woman nudged another and they whispered over the heads of their children, pointing at me with only the hint of finger movement. One of them laughed behind work-wrinkled fingers. I looked down again at the dirt street, at the gutter I was walking in. The fucking gutter! Jesus. I heard an engine behind me, the only one running for blocks around. A big dusty new Ford pickup pulled up next to me. The window slid down into the door. Miss Iowa of 1947 stuck her coiffed gray head out and smiled.

"Habla Usted inglés, señor?"

I puffed up proud so fast I must have scared off half the killer fish for miles around.

"Yes, I do."

"Oh!" she said, embarrassed and delighted. "I thought—oh, well, you just looked. . . ."

Like I belonged! Sonofabitch!

"Could you tell us if there's a telephone here someplace?"

"Yes, ma'am, there is. Just one. It's straight ahead one block past the market place on your left in the gray house. There's a telephone symbol painted on the window."

"Thank you so much." The window climbed up, stopped, and slid back down.

"We hate to impose on you, but we don't know how they do it here. Make the phone calls, that is. And we really don't speak Mexican. . . ."

"Sure, I'll be glad to help you. I'll meet you there."

"Oh, no." she said, opening the door, "you hop in—it's too hot and dirty to walk."

I didn't have the strength to argue, to walk alone so perhaps I wouldn't be seen as belonging to the world of these . . . tourists. I got in. Air conditioned. All I could smell was me. She looked at me, grimaced, then smiled and looked straight ahead while her big, silver-crew-cut husband drove us to the phone station. I got their call placed through the switchboard operator—the only woman I'd seen on the streets in nylons and high heels. I left, turned the corner to my store, and picked up three bottles this time—I had the feeling I wouldn't want to walk through town for a day or two.

It took a long time to get back to my room. I felt like each step was taking me deeper into the side of a giant hot air balloon. The final yards were the hardest: trying to keep my balance in the patio as I sidestepped the mops and buckets the workmen were using for the final cleanup.

Inside the room, I poured a glass of tequila. The smell of it made me gag. I went into the bathroom and threw up. The stopped-up toilet bowl was so full I couldn't sit down anymore without getting my ass wet. I went back into the room, drank the glass empty, lay down, and fell asleep. When I woke up, the light in the room had changed to dusk. I walked across the floor to my suitcase to get a pair of long pants to wear out to catch the end of the sunset. Sand grated under my feet. The maid had stopped coming in to clean the room.

I reached the beach in time to see the horizon swallow the remaining reds of the sunset. I stepped back from the wet quiet of the night onto the veranda. A young man sat at a card table under the one light—a bare lightbulb dangling from the thatched roof. A flip-top box of Mexican cigarettes was tucked into the waistband of a red swim suit against his brown belly. His hands rested on the tabletop surrounded by five or six empty beer cans; a live one stood between his hands. A cigarette drooped from the corner of his lips. His eyes were half closed against the smoke. I made a move to circle around him toward the patio.

"Will you not have a beer with me?" His voice was strong, the edges roughened by the beer. He looked familiar.

"Yes, I will, thank you."

He ordered two beers as I sat down. I stood up, gesturing I would return in a minute. I went back to the room and got a fresh bottle of tequila. When I sat down his hands and the cigarette were in exactly the same position, but the beer in front of me had been opened. Now he stood and motioned for me to wait. He walked just beyond the circle of light and pissed into the sand.

"You do not know me," he said as he sat down, tucking the cigarette pack back into the waistband.

"No."

He smiled and shook his head. I felt uncomfortable and used my eyes to follow my hand as it poured us each a glass of tequila.

"All these days you have walked around me and over me. Perhaps if I turn my back to you then you will know me."

"Perhaps." He did not move.

"My name is José. I am one of the construction workers here. A laborer. You are called Sam. You are also a laborer, but you work on the big boats in San Francisco."

"That is right."

"How is it," he said, pulling the smoking butt from his mouth and dropping it with a hiss into an empty can, "that I know so much of you and you know nothing of me?"

I said nothing and took a titanic swallow of tequila and a sip of beer.

"Is it because I am too small for you to see? After all, we are a small people."

He was almost smiling. Almost.

"Or is it because I have curiosity about a tall American who comes here where few Americans come? Who appears to be a man of warmth but who does nothing but warm the bottles of tequila and a sitting place on the beach. So perhaps it is because I have this kind of curiosity and you do not have it."

"I am sorry for the rudeness."

He waved my words aside gently, leaving a puddle of my growing sadness on the table between us.

"There is nothing to regret," he said, "for now we are friends, true?"

"Truly," I said, reflexively.

He laughed and shook his head.

"Men who drink together, who let their tongues grow loose and long so they reach the heart—are they not friends?"

"José," I said, looking into my glass, "why have you chosen this moment to say these things?"

"Because I am drunk. Because the job is done. Because I leave tomorrow and return to my home in Manzanillo."

"Then it is a sad thing."

"Why?"

"Because we have just become friends."

"But another one comes tonight to you, a tall blonde one."

"But I do not know him."

"Does that matter to you any more?"

"No," I said.

He smiled, again shaking his head.

"Then it would not be a sad thing for you to leave this place also. If you left, then this sadness would remain here and you would be free of it."

Now it was my turn to smile and shake my head.

"It is not yet time for me to leave."

He leaned forward over the table and reached out with his right hand, grasping my left wrist.

"My people," he said, "have a belief. They believe the earth stands still in the sky and the sun moves around her."

He let go of my wrist. I used it to smear the wet beer can stains on the tabletop.

"Is this how you see yourself?" he asked.

"What do you mean?"

"Like the earth, standing still. If you choose, you can be the sun."

"I don't know."

He stood up, steadying himself against the edge of the table.

"I must go, my friend."

"Yes."

"May God go with you."

"And you."

"Until then."

"Until then."

He was gone. Someone turned off the lightbulb from a switch on the patio. I sat for a while, trying to remember the colors of the sunset I had shared with Don and Jeremy, but couldn't. I stood up, stared at the nearly empty tequila bottle, picked it up, and went back to my room.

I lay down on my bed in the dark wearing my clothes and felt a new kind of throw-up sickness fill my body. Footsteps crunched on the patio. The someone stopped outside my door and knocked softly. I got up creaking, turned on the light, and opened the door. The gangly blonde giant had to bend a few degrees to clear the doorway. Two cameras and several lens cases bounced against his narrow chest. Inside the room, he swung an orange back-pack off his shoulders onto the bed and sat down beside it.

"Hello," he said, breathing deeply, "I'm Thor. You must be Sam."

"I am. Welcome. Want a drink?"

"Sure."

I reached for the tequila.

"Oh," he said, "no thanks. I thought you meant juice or something. I'll pass on the booze."

"Sure. Whatever's right. Larry said you were Swedish."

"Norwegian. But I've lived in the States just about all my life. Right now I'm living in Oregon on a spiritual commune."

"Oh."

Thor walked into the bathroom. I watched him stand and stare at the toilet. Suddenly he bent over it and slowly pushed his right arm down into the putrid mess, grabbed hold of something and pulled. The toilet gurgled. He pulled his arm out dripping stink and slime, holding a wad of sopping paper in his hand. With his left hand, he pushed the flush handle. It worked. He turned around as though looking for a garbage can, caught my eyes and smiled. I turned away, reached for my suitcase, and carried it over to my bed.

I heard the shower water start to run, saw his clothes fall on the bathroom floor by the door. I dumped the clothes out of my suitcase, filling it instead with empty tequila bottles. I left while Thor was still in the shower, walked across the patio and cut through the sleeping restaurant to the street. I walked down the block to the corner where the bus to Guadalajara came at dawn with the tortilla smell. I sat down on the curb, with my feet in the gutter and my back against the suitcase filled with trophies to show Jeremy I had done it with style.

Desert

What league you have
With death I do not know
How is that vast expanse
Too vast?

An oceanic feeling overwhelms me.
May it never go away.
The dunes become deceitful stars,
That change their place

In the sky. The arroyos shake
With prickly bushes whose
Fruits and blossoms wait
For a little rain, cracked mud.

Flash flood, flash flood, the
Gully springs to life with
Skittering creatures that rustle
More skeletal than of flesh and blood.

Look! They're afraid of the water
Their very breath of life.
The sun here likewise creates
Its lethal image. This

Very paradox enchants me.
For in it I find a greater
Way of life. No church, no city hall,
Ever let me see a truth,

That was so refined, for
Death lies side by side,
No doubt have I felt it here,
By the barrel cactus.

And when night descends and
The coyotes howl, those prayers
I start to hear. The silence,
Is broken until mid-noon when
Again strange lands appear.

An Orphanage in Guadalajara

Children play in the courtyard,
run to classes in flashes
of Catholic green uniforms
and shy, bound-up smiles,
Fenced off by iron and tour guides
from the central structure
erected long ago with slave-hewn stone.

Blasphemers and dreamers
tip-toe across the tiled terrace
carrying Kodaks and backpacks,
careful not to disturb the centuries
that adorn the corners of
Orozco's turbulent murals.

Dust clouds dangle decadently
in siesta hammocks from the ceiling;
a spider's eye shines in the guardian web,
linked in molecule and memory
to shield emblazoned strokes of painted truth
from mockery and magic markers.

Old Church in Mazatlan

I can't get past the
Wrought-iron gates,
The moon looks over
My shoulder, no shadow.

I'll stand here then
In the bright sunlight.
One question, those travelers
With their tattered bundles

That girdle your waist;
That grisly man in the wheelchair
Made with bicycle chains.
And those wretched Indian women

In black, their beetle-eyed
Urchins begging for pesos.
What can we do for them?
The answer's not inside,

On that fancy golden cross,
Nor in those rainbow windows.
I know you know that too.
I detect an internal sigh.

More tiles fall from your facade;
No one knows but you and I
And the peons on the ladders.
Our strength is the patina

Of the two copper bells
That ring on holy days,
Under cover of night. Let
Us sneak those griffons,

From the lightposts, and
Carry them like candles,
Before the frescos, life.
Star of David, Moorish arches,

Mother of Guadalupe above the
Clock. Senora, Sinaloa, Chihuahua,
Durango, what do we
Care for you?

That old man in the pew?
When it's rainy outside,
He comes in here to sleep.
Right now I hear him dreaming

Of your truest inscription,
"A Perpetuad."

Mexico City

In the Zona Rosa
the antigua cathedrals
thin air, sunlight, music everywhere
horns, bands, guitars, melodic soft Spanish
voices
banners and flowers
Maria Teresa vibrant
tall by comparison to the women
men attentive to her
she glides as she walks
a muscular control in her thighs
her striking style
tarantula hair, black as ink
swift-flowing traffic
police and their big pistolas
women in black shawls smelling
of sunlight and eggs
shoeshine boys and beggars
the firebomb effect of cheap tequila

Maria Teresa
genteel and polite
educated in a convent
for girls with
dignity and social graces
her slender face, profile of a Toltec princess
child of a wedding by Cortes
over her shoulder, the Aztec eagle
the snake and the Mexican flag
Zapata and his handlebar moustache
Juarez who put the whole show on the road
it was always a revelation Villa neither
smoked nor drank
existed in his Wallace Beery style
on young Indian girls
with trim ankles and border raids.

The End of Ben Catlin

Ben sat in the armchair, the one he used as a retreat in the past years, and although the overhead light behind his shoulder illuminated the entire basement in a clear, harsh light, the trunk, piano, and bathtub against the wall were as strange and ominous as they had been on the night he had the DT's. He no longer slept in the bed in the alcove obscured by stacks of newspapers and magazines, but the bed served as a reminder of sleepless nights when he stared at the conduit wires on the ceiling.

He had worked the *Oriana* today, and the gang had finished early. He'd seen the Englishman come down the dock walking erect and stiff, linked arm-in-arm with a woman in dark glasses and a chinchilla coat. The man wore a blue blazer and a regimental tie, and the woman led a poodle on a leash. The dark-winged glasses rested on the pronounced curve of the woman's nose. Ben knew it was impossible for her to be Nola. Although his gang finished early, he waited until almost sailing time, and the woman returned. She came in a limousine after a day of sightseeing, chatting amiably with her companion. She resembled Nola in the structure of her nose, lip, and jaw, but Ben saw that her eyes, without the glasses, were spaced much farther apart, and she had freckles and a British air of gentility that came from playing croquet on lawns rolled for over five hundred years. She ignored Ben as she passed him.

By the time the liner sailed under the Golden Gate bound for the Orient, Ben was home in the garden planting the hydrangea seeds and carefully burying a few nails in with the seed to bring out the blue coloring of the flowers when they bloomed. He heard Lillian moving across the kitchen, and he knew Matthew was in his room doing homework. He opened the desk drawer and as the drawer tilted down a bottle rolled forward. Grabbing the bottle by the neck, he stood it up on the desk. The bottle of Franzia Tokay had two inches of wine left. He stared at the bottle, thoughts running through his head.

He and Lillian no longer started the morning setting traps for each other. It had been impossible to sidestep or avoid all the traps but lately they had found a zone of compromise and the days flew by sandwiched together with no big explosive scenes, no Academy

Award-winning performances inspired by whisky. Lillian still puzzled him. She wanted him to be sober, to work steady, to bring in the big check, because she was considering quitting her job and Ben knew the full meaning behind that move. All the bills, the constant daily economic irritations would be transferred from her shoulders to his. He didn't want to be dependable, not yet, not on the short and anxious and shaky structure of a few months without drinking. She didn't know that fear of a never-ending hallucination kept him from drinking. "Drinking is your baby, you take care of it," she always said. He didn't want her to solve his problems, but he did want understanding. The passion and tender kisses diminished as her complaints increased. If she had to go to work, take care of the house, where did he expect the energy to come from? Exhausted, she always fell to sleep first. Only on the weekends was there any love-making, and that in a contrived and mechanical way. She complained about him being insatiable and horny, and also of his body weight. He suffocated her, smothered her under his weight. Since he had come home and avoided booze, his weight had increased 40 pounds: 282 pounds on the scale at the doctor's office. He had a tireroll around his waist and the extra pounds coincided with the gout that had centered in his toes, increasing the pain that woke him up at night, gasping, in tears. "I hate to hear a fat man cry," she had said.

To Matthew, he had become an everyday Dad, reliable, to be depended on, loved, a helper with the new math. He and the boy had gone out to Candlestick Park to see the Giants play, and although Ben had never been a baseball addict he enjoyed the games, the scrambling for foul balls when they were hit in the stands near them, the hot dogs and coffee. Matthew enjoyed airplanes and to encourage his reactions Ben took him to the airport to watch the jets, silvery birds, luminous in the arclights and after the take-off the rush of noise and wind as the jets rushed into the stars of the sky.

No matter how complaisant his life looked on the surface, a dread pervaded every thought, every action. Had he strangled and buried Nola in the desert, or had he left the institution early with Nola? He constantly thought of Nola and her burial, and each time he confronted the image he decided that it was irrational and that Nola was alive and kicking. The persistent image of her death haunted him. The gnawing sense of guilt made him shiver and twitch around the eyes whenever the phone rang, or someone knocked on the door, or a stranger in a suit walked across the dock and up the gangway to come aboard ship. He was unable to sleep the entire night without waking in a sweat on the verge of panic with the chilling uncertainty as to whether he was a murderer or not. After each nightmare, he wanted to shout for help, without the vaguest notion of what kind or where the help would come from. There was only one solution to this dilemma: Go back to the desert and try to find the makeshift grave.

Ben heard knocking on the ceiling. He shoved the bottle into the drawer, went out to the toolroom and turned out the basement light, shut off the hose in the yard. As he entered the kitchen, Matthew jumped off a chair and onto his back.

"Pop, I gotcha."

Ben reached over his shoulder, hauled the boy around, and sat him in a chair at the table. Lillian brought a ham out of the oven. Ben sliced strips of ham and distributed the slices to the plates. Lillian served the yams, green peas, and mashed potatoes.

After supper, Ben explained to Lillian that he was going fishing for the next two days.

"I'm not going to drink, so don't get on your high horse," he said.

"Why not wait until the weekend when the boy is finished with school?"

"Too crowded. People crawling over each other, lines tangled."

"How long will you be gone?"

"Two days. I may leave tonight, be there in the morning, fish at daybreak, fish at dusk. I should be home the very next day." He knew the cincher. "This way I can be back to work the weekend."

"You're going to do it your own way," Lillian said. "You always do and always will."

"Don't get us into a hassle over a two-day trip."

"I know a promise means nothing, but try not to drink."

"This trip is not a subterfuge."

"I hope not."

Suddenly he resented Lillian with her dark hair over her shoulders, the even white teeth, and her scent of cologne. She had a way of intruding into problems that didn't concern her. He had enough worries with the steady, prolonged, unreasoned instinct that pulled him toward the canyon. He didn't want to argue with Lillian, leave the house in a turmoil to duplicate the turmoil within himself. So he and Lillian made their peace, a Mexican truce of sorts, Dad going to fish, life as usual. God Bless Our Happy Home.

He drove all night only stopping for gas and black coffee. When he arrived in Barstow, in the dead of summer now, people moved in the shade like phantoms, trying to dodge the direct rays of the sun. Only a short time away from the canyon, tense with anticipation, he knew he had to have an edge, a release. For the first time in his life, he understood this was not a rationalization. He had to have something to combat the heat, at least a beer, and a booster whisky to calm him down as he approached the arroyo. Methodically he drove to the nearest grocery store and bought a case of beer and a quart of Early Times. At the hardware store, he purchased a washtub and filled it with a block of ice from the coin-operated icehouse. With his pocket knife, he broke the ice into chunks and placed the cans of beer along the sides of the tub. The tub sat on the back seat, within easy reach. He kept the whisky in a paper bag. On the way to Chambliss, he sipped the whisky and pulled over to the side of the road periodically to open cans of beer, the liquid cool and yeasty. The heat rose in waves from the asphalt, and there was a mirage ahead. His last visit over two months ago was a balmy picnic compared with the Mojave today. The layers of heat made the sky a hard, cruel yellow that pressed down the waterless, treeless, birdless waste of sand.

There were very few cars on the road, and once he turned off at the beginning of the Old Woman Mountains he encountered no one. The dust from the road alongside the Atcheson Topeka & Santa Fe tracks was a fine powder that billowed behind the car. The ice had almost melted, and the remaining cans of beer bobbed and floated in the water. When he turned into the wide arroyo, the dust settled and the arroyo floor was harder and firmer packed than the road. He searched for the landmarks that might indicate the canyon.

The heat made him irritable. After walking into a canyon that had the remembered high wall entrance but didn't continue in a curve, he came back to the car and drank three beers in a row. He checked the whisky—three-quarters gone. The effect of the whisky was minimal; no doubt the heat burned out the alcohol, burned the sugar, sizzled his brain. The heat had neutralized the whisky, and as he drank there was no burning sensation in his throat. He decided to try one more canyon. If it was only an hallucination, there might not be any canyon at all. Then an idea came to him almost as a revelation. Maybe he was at the wrong end of the quest. Why hadn't he thought of the apartment in San Francisco: Bust in and find Nola in her front room with the walls plastered with grave rubbings of old movie stars. Nola in the midst of a party or seance, captivating and charming, the center of attention, surrounded by astrologers and spirit seekers, surprised at his entrance.

When he drove into the next canyon, blood drained from his face, the sense of terror and expectancy caused his hands to tremble. He parked the station wagon near the ocotillo. Too weak to climb from the car, he drank two more cans of beer. When he tried to light a cigar, his hands shook so much that it required five matches. In the hospital in Barstow and up in the city he may have had doubts, but in the canyon beside the ocotillo the supposed hallucination became a reality. A coordination of instinct and intellect told him the truth. He was here in fact, a corporeal body of flesh and blood and before him the grave of the women he had strangled. Gathering his strength, dripping with sweat, sweat that wet the inner part of his pants and crotch, shaking knees, he took the shovel from the back and started to dig. The pain of sun burning on the top of his head made him go back to the car for the white cap, the one he used aboard ship. Snapping the brim to shade his eyes, he started digging again. The click of the shovel on loose rock loud as a pistol shot in the desolate canyon.

Beneath the top layer of sand, the ground was too hard. No, no one had ever dug here before. In a slow and exhausting process, he dug down four feet and then he started a series of exploratory holes in a half circle around the ocotillo, and he nearly fainted from the heat. Nothing. For a moment he had a sense of relief, a release from guilt, a feeling that made him jump up, click his heels, throw his hat in the air, the idea of being reborn. And he thought of the day their dog, Billy Friend, 57 varieties, more terrier than anything else, died: ate a meal of scraps, turned over on his back and died. Dad sent them to the store for candy, and while he and Wally were gone, dug a hole in the ground and buried the dog nose down, tail out of the ground. When they returned munching on licorice, only the tail protruded from the ground and on it a small sheet of paper wrapped with a string, written in pencil, "the end of billy friend." If he had paper, he might write, "the end in my life of Nola Robideaux." But he was tired of playing games, of performing. He only wanted to return home. When he thought of the heat and how far he was from the asphalt highway, the sense of joy evaporated. He had never been this hot, the drops of sweat stung his pores. The air quivered, and the sun vibrated heat, and the hood of the station wagon assumed a searing white glow. His heart palpitated. Each move became painful. When he touched the door-handle, his hand jerked away as if he'd had an electric shock. The metal of the station wagon was as hot as a pot bellied stove, red-metal, steel-edge hot. Tender-fingered, he opened the door. He had to sit down and recapture his breath, and he knew he had to conserve his strength. As he thought about the long distance back to the highway, he thought of the shortcut his Dad always used whenever he went up to the spring on the high plateau at the east side of the Old Woman Mountain, the spring with the Joshua, palm, and cottonwood trees. Only he would use the hogback on the spine going down the opposite side to the dry lake. It was a hardbed lake and could support the car, and by maintaining a northeast direction he'd connect with the highway by using this quicker and shorter route. Immediately Ben felt better.

The hogback veered to the right, and he stayed in the ruts of a jeep trail winding down from the spine to the eastward away from the big arroyo and the railroad tracks toward a dry lake. The alkali bed of the lake stretched out for miles with a road heading northeast. His eyes smarted and he turned around; there were only two cans of beer in tepid water in the tub. He splashed water on his head and neck, his eyes blinked and smarted, and without seeing the sign he drove past it. NAVY BOMBING RANGE. In red letters below, OUT OF BOUNDS, and below, in smaller letters, how and by what code one was to be prosecuted if one ignored the sign. The sun was high in the sky and directly behind him; before him, the powdery road due north; he hoped the wagon and the motor lasted until he reached the main highway.

Puzzled, he wondered what was up ahead—a mirage of cars? A junkyard of cars? When he came closer, he saw that it was not a mirage. There were at least a hundred cars parked sideways, but in a direct line. He drank the last beer and tried to remember when he urinated last—not since the canyon. The sweat oozed from his pores by the bucketful. He drew a rag through the remaining water, hung it around his neck, dipped the white cap, and pulled it atop his head. He stepped from the wagon. Waves of heat shimmered from the cars. Most of them were old, none later than a 1965; some were mashed and had obviously been in wrecks. A few were intact; weathered gray paint, U.S. Navy insignias on the doors, government plates.

In the stillness he heard a plane, high overhead but coming louder. Squinting his eyes, he saw sun reflect from the silvery metal. The plane had turned and was heading toward him. Plodding, but quickly, Ben returned to the wagon and drove it into line with the other cars. With a black rush of wind and forceful power, the jet raced overhead ,and directly over the tops of the wrecks, the pull-away, a lightning streak of silver and vapor. Ben judged its speed at 800 miles an hour. From the first moment he sighted the jet, a tiny sliver of reflection, it had only taken a few minutes to race low, lightning fast to envelop him in a rush of noise and earth-shaking velocity. He sat still, heart pumping, eyes tracking the plane clean over the Old Woman Mountains, higher and higher, disappearing. Terrified and shaken, he came out of the car.

He caught the sliver of streaking light to the east, the plane again. In a few beats of his heart, he watched the completion of the circle, the sudden onrush of wings, the engulfing wind, the spouts of sand as bullets hit the ground, rattled into the old wrecks, a hailstorm of steeljacketed destruction, finite, pure.

The sudden bumps that shivered him, the sledgehammer impact, the bone-shattering crack, spun Ben knocking him to the sand, sudden, incomprehensible. Eyes glazed, he saw the Navy insignia under the wings. Struggling to his feet, part of his jaw peeled, fell away in his hands, staggering, blood spouting from the sieveholes in his body onto the alkali bed.

He waved an arm, the word *stop* gargled in blood as he lurched, his knees twisting askew, broken-legged he fell forward, bouncing from the back of an old sedan, sixth in line from the wagon, smearing blood on the bumper, to roll and collapse, nose drenched in blood and alkali powder. The frame of his body stretched on the hot and scorching sand, multiple holes clean through. His feet moved to raise him from a prone position, but only pushed his nose deeper into the dust.

In his imagination he returned to his childhood, before he ever knew of violence and booze. The day Wally received his first football from Mom, they were both in knickers. Ben felt himself spiral, borne upward on death spasms, up as high as Wally spiraled the bright, new, birthday pigskin, higher and higher . . . into the sky above the ballpark, and he sat beside Matthew munching on hot dogs, drinking root beer, watching the flyballs, the grounders, and if they were lucky, a home run, safe in the knowledge that Lillian was home preparing a bangup supper, hair combed neat, body perfumed and clean smelling, earrings dangling, ready for the long night under the halo of the moon, the boy asleep, Ben had to laugh, the night the bed collapsed, one end crashed down, and they continued on the rug of the bedroom floor.

He had thought of death before, and in his images he never died in bed but squashed by a van when a fall line parted, or have a boom escape as it was being lowered, crush him to the deck, or in an auto wreck, or to accidentally shoot himself on a hunting trip. He had never thought of a Navy plane, the cannonading of target bullets, death on a dry soda lake, in the shadow of the Old Woman Mountains. The thin flake of alkali, the sweet, powdery taste of lime. Dear Jesus, although I am a drunk, I am also a father and deserve more than a death among junked cars, a human target, steeljacketed clean through. The glare of the dry lake turning to gray and a hollow darkness that smelled like the confines of a warm sweet dungeon. Tight across the chest, pinned by a giant boom, jawless, not even able to talk, and his consciousness rapidly evaporating into fine dust.

His hands, clutched into fists gave a convulsive jerk. He reached over the grass at the edge of the dwarf milo, gypsy corn, trying to recover Wally's football, encircle the pigskin, thumb near the end, and the tips of his fingers, all four fingers on the lacing. Under the ornaments on the crucifix arms of the Joshua tree, the sound of carols, warmed by the bonfire, his mother placed her hand on his shoulder and her shawl covered them both. . . . One leg in the fender shadow of the old sedan, blood drippings dried by the burning bulb of the sun, the end of Ben Catlin. Ben Catlin lay dead.

Ireland

Dublin I

Shaving in a Martello Tower
    is forbidden now.
I know a man who did it, though.
He also sold 19 keys to 7 Eccles St.
All said to be original.

Desmond is his first name
And I met him coming through
A window, beating the rent.
He has a scapular and a pierced
Heart of Jesus
Hanging on the wall,
Trades on artists' goods and
Sixth senses
The only soft spot in his heart
Is for a girl
"Beautiful artist," he says
Always has bandages on her wrist.
He sleeps with her,
Keeps her from suicide.
He always says, "The blood of an
Artist can heal a nation."

Dublin II

Soot from ancient peat fires
Thick on the buildings.
The dole, Danegold children
Living solefully over the
hulls of Viking ships
and ancient relics.

Railroad South to North
Running to the heartland
of Cuchulain.

Cars clacking by
the barnacled brood
sent down to fight the tide.
Guinness bottle brown bodies
Seaweed, snot-green sea.
Death masks with Extreme Unction smiles,
Wolf Tone and Robert Emmett, Kilmainhem Jail
Darkened cells and sunlit execution yards.
Everyone knows the others' business
and on opposite sides of the city
wired electrodes await the connecting arc.

Glendalough

Two-tiered lake, slow running water.
The land grazed on, raised on,
prayed on for centuries.
Stone hermitages a constant theme.
Singular souls near clear slow water.
It always takes its time. Flow and time.
It ran over Viking raiders and British troops.

Round lookout towers the only note of difference.
Stones returning to the land
from their highborn position
placed by man.
One tier spills to the other, lake and building,
slow,
Where only the most sentient know
time is always and always is
the water to the sea, graze and grouse,
Moment of the spirit,
Bog and wooded road lead down to a table
of land, a shaded cottage. The artist's hermitage.
He will tell you all the secrets
of his ancestral land, connecting layers,
and produce for you the art of centuries,
from Ireland to Galatia, Asia Minor to Glendalough,
He welds jewelry, Celtic completions,
spiral secrets of falling land, wandering people.

ROBERT CARSON

Road Gangs

Ireland has traveling road crews
work gangs that sleep by their
patches of pavement—in tents.
They follow the lines of falling land,
From their hands come the cement
that holds the Republic together.

They know the stone homes
returning to the land, piece by falling piece,
the thatched roofs of Adare,
the barren of the Burren,
Lakes of Kilarney where their brothers
on jaunting cars hustle: "Looking fer
the good ride, best tour, I kin show ya
mister, yes missus."

They patch roads, stay off the dole
with gypsy guile and free-born swing
the work army rises every morning
across the country, cold balance of water and air,
poems and reels still wrapped in midnight
to be sung on mended trail between

Wandering rocks, solid stones of graveyards,
the Celtic spiral, fall and return,
weavers and menders place together
ancient rituals, ways of work, threadbare lives.
With their hands they are the transmission line
of the road ever on.

In Dublin they drink with city
industrial workers.
Border of international trade,
Blood and muscle of revolution, failure,
Dream of return.
The electric shock, connected electrodes
Raise the night only to meet the road and sun.
In cross-town bars, 11 PM curfew
Struggling old men don sunglasses, aching eyes,
hit the road, leaving younger men—road gangs
and workers—the patched dreams:
Blind poets, Fenian gods, and future organization.

Sligo

Long strands like gnarled hands
Fall sloping to the sea.
Fingers of the poet in the land,
gypsies roam, Lake Isles,
Queen Maeve's Cairn,
megalithic remains.
From twisted trumpet shells
the sound goes out—
eternal waves from Innisfree
to the coast.

What ancient work army built the cairn
or all the single stone slabs thrust up
and now canted back to the land?
Moonscape or graveyard from the past?
When the tide goes out, showing the shells,
late northern day, sun at 10 PM,
Come the ancient cars of Ilium—
the sand stretched tight down a beach,
glistening quick mask—dampened smell of history.
Workman's sweat, poet's sanguine soul.

Behind the beach,
Walk up the Strand,
Lane crowded with reeds and wild flowers,
11 PM senses go wild,
Stand on the knuckles of land,
turn to the sea,
sun-exploded horizon, curragh ideas
survive upon the water.
And riding up from the beach,
Irish gypsies and worker-horsemen
challenge the falling land.

GENE DENNIS

Seascape

The dune
bulging white
behind the faded
red house.

The dune
crawling with
green ice plant
moves warm
against the
kitchen door.

The dune
defending against
ocean wind
scatters sand
on the window sill.

The dune:
Impending.

J. PRICE

Holy Communion

How is it I watch the sea,
Those gray clouds, the mountains,
Silhouetted against the void,
Everything so still today.

I search for the reason,
but it does not come.
The waves mark time like
A corps of drummers leads

The foolhardy into war.
Then what is it, where is it,
The answer, I mean, to
This ridiculous life.

Oh, look there, time flies
A fish hawk, the mountains, the
Sea, the sky, what perfection
We lose to eternity.

Motor Vessel "Viking Raider"
San Francisco Bay: Jan. 3, 1973
Final Hours

I wish I could say we were in the Sargasso Sea or somewhere romantic like that, but we can't even get out of San Francisco Bay. The entire crew is drunk, as usual. It's been two and one-half weeks since I signed on at the Seamen's Hall, thinking I'd get to Chile on the *Raider* so I could finally see Pilar.

We spent weeks together in my Mission District flat while she made up her mind to either stay with me or go to a teaching job in Santiago. The lure of a new and developing world, the key to South America, the *penas* and propositions from all the men drew her.

Two years ago at Christmas time, we said goodbye. I couldn't stand another Christmas around the city so I signed on the *Raider*, and we're stuck in this fucking bay for two and one-half weeks. An international crew on board. One Greek, a Spaniard, and several Norwegians; they accuse the Spaniard of stealing their soap, the Spaniard accuses the Greek, and he's been giving me the fish eye lately.

No one has seen the captain in weeks, and there's a rumor he doesn't even exist. I caught sight of him once, shooting into his quarters. Large bandage on the right side of his face reminds me of the Van Gogh self-portrait with mutilated ear. The other rumor is he was a U-boat commander in World War II. He has a torpedo build, but I think it all stops there. The strongest and craziest of all the lunatics on board is Calvin McNaught. Fortunately, he took a liking to me early on. Says he's a fallen Catholic from "Upper Ireland, the Occupied Part." A hurler's build—agile, strong, fast, lady-killer, body of granite, angular-cut face under curling black hair.

A fourteen-year-old kid shares my *fo'csle*. I share nothing with him, and he only smiles and cannot speak English. Loves music, though. He has a cassette recorder and plays "When Sonny Gets Blue" over and over. They all have recorders and just enough money to stay drunk for the rest of their lives.

Calvin and I reminisce about Olsen's Last Rest in Venezuela. I had been there on my twenty-fifth birthday a few years ago when Olsen was still alive. The sailor's dream—Olsen hit the jackpot on a national lottery, only he couldn't take the money out of the country, so he buys a bar, treats all the seamen, and drinks himself to death. Everyday, all day, sitting on the wooden bar stool, straining slowly into oblivion. A year later Olsen died, and I was in port the night new owners took over. Biggest riot I'd ever seen. Calvin loves this story.

I asked him, "Do you really think the old man's a Nazi?"

"Just cause he keeps yelling 'Up periscope' don't prove nothin', lad."

"You've seen him, then," I said.

"That shrimp son of a bitch. Sure I have. Listen, I know men who could outnavigate and outman him with *both* hands tied behind their backs."

"Yeah." I was incredulous.

"Look, laddie, I like you 'cause you're Irish, even though you were born in America. But your hair and eyes. Why, they're too goddamn much like the squareheads here. Consequently, I conclude they're right about you. You're a damn Irish Viking."

Colors are darkening down the bay, the curvature of sky. Nightfall locking us in one more time. Still tied up bow and stern to Pier 50. Colors: maroon to cobalt. I can envision us in deep water, plunging and cutting up waves. Every day closer to Santiago. Got my eye on the cargo in Number One Hatch, upper 'tween deck. Ten tons of Kool-Aid for the starving masses of South America, so I know we'll make the run down the coast. A lot of tramps change course quicker than the winds. Once I thought I was going to South America, and many drunken days later we were in Hamburg.

From Pier 50 I can see Potrero Hill and up through the Mission. Behind them, Twin Peaks and the fog cascading over the hills, something Pilar and I loved to watch. The hills with fog rolling down. The coast's breathing ritual with interior valleys. The fog rising in Alaskan tundra dreams, cold and wet, liquid flux of tundra drawn down and in by the heat of valleys, all interconnected to the Mexican border.

We have three women on the ship. A radio operator and two mess girls who wait primarily on the officers. Calvin and I watch them stagger up the gangway. "Shame, you know," he says. "That radio broad is good-looking, too." He lit a cigarette. "They've been over to the Greek ship there." He pointed up Islais Creek, where a ship seemed to be moored to the buildings of the financial district.

"One day soon, I mean very soon, they'll throw a couple of lines around the TransAmerica building, plug the ship into a computer and that's it for us."

"There'll always be jobs," I said, half-heartedly.

"No, laddie, no. This is the last gasp, you know. I can hear the death rattle, sounds like the electric whip of falls on cranes and people gettin' devoured by money and big homes."

The three women make the top of the gangway. "Shame," Calvin says. "The Scandahoovians would rather drink than fuck. So the women gotta go to a Greek ship for some fun."

"How do you know?"

"Look, you just signed on, but the rest of us been followin' this Greek freighter across the seven seas. Seems everywhere they are, we are. You know how money follows money. The Kool-Aid circuit, then bauxite from Surinam. Oh, Christ." He began wiping his brow. I had the distinct feeling that he was going to cry. He tugged on a bottle under his coat. "You see, if you don't measure things out properly, pay out just enough line in this life, then this tin fish we're on becomes a floating insane asylum."

Nils the cook is gesturing wildly from the bridge.

"Speaking of insanity." Calvin shrugs a look up.

"Go on. I'm stayin' here," Calvin says.

Nils is wrecked, blasted out of his socks. He wants me to drink with him. The cycle was starting on me again, the beautiful spiral descent. Booze, sorrow over Pilar, self-pity, night and fog, terror, rats in the hold gnawing on the lines and sniffing around the Kool-Aid. And we are still in port. At this rate I might be in Chile by next winter. Since it's summer there during our winter, I wanted to see Pilar now. The magic words "Have another drink." Fifteen men on a dead man's chest, and all that bullshit. Christ, the times we had stumbling around San Francisco together. She in a floppy hat, like some Impressionist painter had put her together, or Levi's and socialist meetings. I never understood why she dragged me to so many different socialist groups and meetings. Pretty soon I think I became the test animal. A real worker, get him, dissect him, find out why he's the backward brute he is. And Pilar with those green eyes, flashing, black, shining hair. Her Spanish mother, Andalusian anarchist; Irish father, longshoreman and veteran of the 1934 general strike. Pilar was tall but still wore the stacked heels like shorter women, and this cast her thin hips and round ass into a sensual waddle. Her skin brown, but not like the beer-bottle-brown of the South Americans and Mexicans who lived near us.

Nils, in a total stupor, "Do you know why the Nazis invaded Norway, young man?"

"Why?" I hated being called "young man."

"Oh, I'm not going to tell you that easily. You must promise not to spread it around. I'm telling you this because I know you can take care with it. If it falls into the wrong hands, there will be scholars rewriting history and people getting grants from the Ford Foundation. But this is our secret, the Norwegian people's secret. The Nazis never found out."

"What, Nils! What?" I was yelling and impatient.

He looked drunkenly straight into my eyes and grabbed my sleeve to steady himself. "Turn your ear to me," he began turning my head for me. Then, in deep, low intonations, "The Nazis invaded Norway for our margarine recipe. But we never cracked, we never gave it to them. You know that big dollop of margarine I put in the soup every day? Well, that's still the same secret. Someday I will show you how to make it."

The thought of his soup, Nazis, his blood pudding—a daily ration—made me want to throw up. But if I got sick it would be all over Calvin or the women just below me, so I tried to keep it in.

Now the sky is pouring down black into the sea; I feel blood-drained and anemic-sick; gulls with bled-white wings angling and cutting every which way. How long I've been drinking, I have no idea. Something like the longest night of the year. A short bus ride to my flat in the Mission, a short boat ride to open water.

A sudden loosening. Must be a wake from some passing vessel in the bay. But no. No lines any more. The fourteen-year-old kid, my cabin mate, is heaving lines. They learn fast. In every port, someone gets our lines, standard operation on a tub like this. They go to the highest bidder. Now the kid is throwing every piece of rope he can find, and linesmen on the dock are cheering and waving goodbye. I can't believe it. Finally underway. The skyline is moving. Nils pulls me inside.

"The captain will want to see that young boy. You don't want to be a witness."

Inside, I notice all the corridors I've scrubbed down for two and one-half weeks. They're hospital white, and I feel like someone is covering my mouth and nose with ether. They want me to pass out so they can take me apart and use me for what they want. "We have ways of making you talk. You have been noticed going to socialist meetings." They're taking off the velvet gloves, and they slam me in the mouth.

Nils grabs me as I hit the walls trying to make my way down the corridor. Blood pours from the side of my mouth. Might as well drink compass alcohol and get it over with.

A voice, booming through the corridors: male, basso profundo, ringing through the hallways. Sounds like one of the Norwegians in agony.

"What does he say?" I ask Nils.

"It's the captain," he answered.

"Yes, but what is he saying? I don't understand Norwegian."

Nils listens, weaving back and forth, his brow furrowed and intense. "He says he's seasick."

"Seasick!" I screamed. "We aren't even out of the bay yet."

"He is sick of the sea. It cannot comfort him. He has computed that we will not make Rotterdam in six weeks and his wife will leave him."

I can hear McNaught singing Gaelic folksongs and tickling women. The tapes are rolling. From the captain's cabin, sounds like music from the Siegfried cycle. As I approach my *fo'csle* below, "When Sonny Gets Blue."

Tafetta waves and a black sky coffin. Is that the captain yelling "Dive, dive!"? A high fog over the city hills, with open patches and the moon spinning. Pilar in a light summer dress that clings suggestively to her body in the warm breezes. At a distance on the bay, four lights. Look, I know for a fact Van Gogh painted at night with candles on his hat and easel. Blood is drying at the side of my mouth. I must smell like a cross between a slaughter house and a distillery.

Pilar, if I could be there, I'd take both of us to the Andes, as high up and far away from the sea as possible. Watch the summer color, bring music off the wind through a flute, bring life to both of us. If you wanted, I'd marry you; your slender hips and tall, slim body. Hold on to the earth away from the tides. Let go of my seed. See summer flowering on the plains.

Now you are a memory. Sailing. A thousand ideas turn around you. You are at the center of me. Ideas go slipping through my fingers. You stay. I take you with me in this heartland of the winter.